MITS, WITS AND LOGIC

Books with text by Lillian R. Lieber
and drawings by Hugh Gray Lieber

The Education of T. C. Mits
(W. W. NORTON & COMPANY, INC.)

The Einstein Theory of Relativity
(HOLT, RINEHART & WINSTON)

Take a Number
(RONALD PRESS COMPANY)

Galois and the Theory of Groups
(GALOIS INSTITUTE PRESS)

Non-Euclidean Geometry
(GALOIS INSTITUTE PRESS)

Good-bye Mr. Man, Hello Mr. NEWman
(GALOIS INSTITUTE PRESS)

Mits, Wits and Logic
(W. W. NORTON & COMPANY, INC.)

Infinity
(HOLT, RINEHART & WINSTON)

Comedie Internationale
(GALOIS INSTITUTE PRESS)

Lattice Theory: The Atomic Age in Mathematics
(GALOIS INSTITUTE PRESS)

Human Values and Science, Art and Mathematics
(W. W. NORTON & COMPANY, INC.)

MITS
WITS
and
LOGIC

Text by
LILLIAN R. LIEBER

Drawings by
HUGH GRAY LIEBER

Third Edition

NEW YORK
W. W. Norton & Company, Inc.

PRINTED IN THE UNITED STATES OF AMERICA

67890

This little book
is affectionately dedicated to

YOU

in the hope that
you CARE
and will
DO SOMETHING
about
all
this.

PREFACE

This is not intended to be
free verse.
Writing each phrase on a separate line
facilitates rapid reading,
and everyone
is in a hurry
nowadays.

PREFACE TO THE SECOND EDITION

In the main, this second edition is the same as the first –
some minor corrections were made, the situation with
respect to modern bombs has been brought up to date.
But, as regards the antiquated courses in Logic in most
colleges, they are still being given, and therefore this survey
of how they can be improved by the introduction of
Boolean Algebra, is still in order. And SAM is still
waiting to help us.

Since the book was first published, it has been read by
the great logician, Rudolf Carnap, who was good enough
to say: "Not only did I find 'Mits, Wits and Logic'
exceedingly well done and the drawings inspired and
charming, but I was highly gratified to find there the
impressive connection of the scientific material with
your Weltanschauung, and I am delighted that you too
are so deeply impressed with the necessity of avoiding
another war. That is just my feeling that in the present
situation the elimination of war is paramount to all the
other issues."

I trust the reader will agree that this not only holds
good in 1954, but it is imperative that this point of view
be EMPHASIZED at this time, in the hope that it will
become universal and really effective so that we may
eliminate not alone war itself, but also the threat and the
fear of war, and direct our energy and our wealth to the
many human needs all over the world. This is my prayer.

L. R. L.

PREFACE TO THE THIRD EDITION

Everything that was in the Preface to the
Second edition, still holds good now, in 1960!
Chapters II and III have been brought up to date.
But of course Part II on "Realism, Modern Style,"
and Part III on "Logic" are as good as ever.
And again I repeat, as in Part I, "The Emergency":

WAR MUST STOP HERE AND NOW!

Or else!
This is still my prayer.

L. R. L.

CONTENTS

ACKNOWLEDGMENT

I take pleasure in acknowledging my
thanks to Professor Ernest Nagel of the
Department of Philosophy of Columbia University
for reading this entire book in manuscript,
for his enthusiastic expression of approval of it,
and for making several valuable suggestions.

L. R. L.

PART I

THE EMERGENCY

I. INTRODUCING SAM

Those of you who
have met Mits before
know that he is
the celebrated
Man-In-The-Street.*

From which you can guess that
Wits
is the
Woman-In-The-Street.

Both of them are
anxious to meet
SAM,
who, they have heard,
can help them to
get along in this
Modern World.

Mits begs you
NOT to mistake him for
Mitts,
who believes that
MIGHT makes RIGHT!

And Wits does NOT want
to be mistaken for
one who "wittily"
tweaks his neighbor's nose,

* See "The Education of T. C. Mits"
  by Lillian R. Lieber,
  with drawings by
  Hugh Gray Lieber
  (W. W. Norton & Company, 1944).

15

saying,
"Whatsa matter,
ain't you got
no sense o' humor?"

Mits and Wits
are
merely the two billion
men and women
who want
TO LIVE AND LET LIVE,
and who would like to ask
SAM
the $64 question:
"HOW?"

But who is this character,
SAM?
And what makes them think
that he
can help us?

To say that his name
is derived from
Science,
Art and
Mathematics
may leave you cold,
for you may say:
"I grant that
   Scientists,
   Artists,
   Mathematicians
   have done some wonderful things,
   BUT
   when it comes to getting us out of
   the horrible mess in which

16

the whole world now finds itself—
they are
no wiser and no better
than the rest of us.
And so
if that is all you have to offer,
please count me out!"

And of course
you are quite right—
for you have probably
seen or heard of
some scientists and mathematicians
who are rational enough while
they are working on
one of their own problems,
but who,
as soon as they come away
from their desks and laboratories,
are as irrational as
the rest of us—
just as some
so-called "religious" people
are "good" on Sundays
and pirates on
all the other days of the week.

But SAM himself is
DIFFERENT.
For he is the
ESSENCE of
what is best in
Science,
Art,
Mathematics,
and therefore is
good and true and beautiful
on all the days of the week

and is always available
to guide and help us
if we would but
go to him.

But "HOW?"

II. A MESSAGE FROM SAM

Here is an illustration of
how SAM is trying
to help us,
if we would only listen!

Recently *
Einstein and
some Atomic Physicists
made the following statements:

(1) Atomic bombs can now be made
    cheaply and in large number.
    They will become MORE destructive.*

(2) There is NO military defense
    against atomic bombs and
    NONE is to be EXPECTED.†

(3) Other nations can rediscover
    our secret processes
    by THEMSELVES.

* This was written in the
  first edition, 1947,
  but is still of interest
  because it shows how long ago
  the Atomic Physicists foresaw and warned us
  about our dilemma of TODAY, in 1960!
  How long will it take us to find out that
  SAM is not only competent
  but has a profound understanding of
  and love for
  The Human Race!
  He wants LIFE for the human race
  in spite of all its failings!

(4) Preparedness against atomic war
is FUTILE, and
if attempted, will RUIN
the structure of
our social order.

(5) If war breaks out,
atomic bombs WILL be used
and they will SURELY DESTROY
our CIVILIZATION.

(6) There is no solution
to this problem
EXCEPT
the ELIMINATION of WAR.

And yet
some people are ignoring this
WARNING
and are advocating
"strong defense measures,"
more bombs,
biological means such that
a small bottle of the stuff
may be at least
as "strong" as an atomic bomb,
and can be made cheaply
in an innocent-looking "brewery,"
so that even international "control"
would be impossible.
Biological warfare has not received
as much publicity as
atomic-bomb warfare,

but SAM strongly advises you to
acquaint yourself with it!
Well, please read again
SAM'S SIX-POINT WARNING
given above,
and you will see how right SAM was.
For atomic bombs have indeed become more destructive—
there are now hydrogen bombs,
Intercontinental ballistic MISSILES (ICBM's)
(and there are no ANTI-missile missiles!).
Other nations have indeed got these now,
and more nations are getting ready to make them!
Everyone now agrees that
World War III would indeed
SURELY DESTROY CIVILIZATION,
if not the whole human race!
Indeed,
COMPLETE DISARMAMENT is even now
being discussed—
this is NOT an easy problem to solve
and will take much TIME and PATIENCE—
but the alternatives are so much worse that
even our President Eisenhower and
some of his own Generals
(like General Power, for instance, as well as others)
disagree among themselves as to whether or not,
for example,
to keep our bombers with the most terrible bombs,
up in the air around the clock,
twenty-four hours a day,
in case the Soviet Union
pulls a "Pearl Harbor" with ICBM's.
Power says yes, Eisenhower says no,
and the people are of course
terribly confused by all this!
And so, I say again,
let us listen to point (6) of SAM's warning (p. 21),

for SAM, as you have seen, is still
our best prognosticator! (see footnote on p. 20).
"But," you may say,
"why do you call this SAM's warning,
when it is really only the opinion of some scientists;
they are of course entitled to their opinion in a
Democracy,
but so am I entitled to my own opinion,
and I don't agree with them,
that's all."
To which the answer is of course:
This is NOT a matter of opinion,
but a matter of SCIENTIFIC FACTS,
a domain in which the scientists
KNOW what they are talking about,
and mere "opinion," like yours and mine,
has nothing to do with the case.

So you see that
in matters of SCIENCE
we MUST NOT take the
INCOMPETENT advice of anyone,
regardless of how we may value
his friendship and good sense in other things.
For here is a domain in which
SAM,
not Mother,
"KNOWS BEST!"

III. THE MODERN PAUL REVERE

"Well," you say,
"suppose we grant that
your ideal,
SAM,
is right in maintaining
that it would be wonderful
if war were eliminated.
But what can we,
Mits and Wits and
all the little Mits-Wits,
DO ABOUT IT?
Obviously nothing, for
war is just a part of
human nature—
there was always war,
and always will be.
So,
being helpless to stop it,
let's forget about the bombs, etc.,
and have us a good time
as long as we can.
And when the end comes,
it will all be over
in a few minutes anyway,
so why worry?"

To which SAM replies:
"What makes you think that
you will be
one of the lucky ones who
will die instantly?
Have you read the description of

what really happened in
Hiroshima? *

Do you know that
some of those people
are still alive and
suffering from hideous diseases,
some of the effects of which
will appear even in
their children and grandchildren?
No,
death is NOT the worst thing
that modern warfare brings!"

And therefore let us ask
SAM
what we CAN DO about it,
hoping that he will remember
that
we humans cannot
"take it"
as he can—
we need a little rest and recreation,
Mits representing the
tired businessman—
and Wits may have been
standing over a hot stove
all day!

SAM is of course
most sympathetic with Wits,
telling her that
she really need not
stand over a hot stove
these days,
for there are pressure-cookers

* See *Hiroshima* by John Hersey
  (Alfred A. Knopf, 1946).

and all sorts of conveniences in
his gadget department
for her.
And,
as regards rest and recreation,
his staff of
physicians,
psychologists,
psychiatrists
and others
are fully aware of this,
and heartily agree that
they are essential for
Mits and Wits.
So we see that
SAM has a heart,
and is definitely
FOR us.
And it is exactly BECAUSE
he is our friend
that he is warning us that
the TIME HAS COME
for eliminating war—
or ELSE!

Furthermore,
he believes that YOU,
Mits and Wits,
CAN DO it.
That is why he got
the Atomic Scientists
not only to
announce the above-mentioned
six-point warning,
but to act as
the modern Paul Revere
to arouse the entire country
to an awareness of the

BUSINESS AS USUAL

DANGER.
That is why
Professor Einstein sent the following
TELEGRAM TO THE PEOPLE:

Our world faces crisis
as yet UNPERCEIVED by those
possessing power to make
great decisions for good or evil.
Unleashed power of the atom
has CHANGED EVERYTHING
EXCEPT our modes of THINKING
AND WE THUS DRIFT TOWARD
UNPARALLELED CATASTROPHE.
We scientists who released this immense power
have overwhelming responsibility
in this world-wide life-and-death struggle
to harness atom
for BENEFIT of MANKIND
and NOT for humanity's destruction.
Bethe, Condon, Szilard, Urey and
Federation of American Scientists
join me in this appeal
and beg you to support
our efforts to bring realization to America
that mankind's destiny is being decided
TO-DAY, NOW, THIS MOMENT!
We need $200,000 AT ONCE †
for NATIONWIDE CAMPAIGN

† Since this was written, this money and more was raised
   and the people have become much better informed concerning
   Atomic Energy—
   its potentialities for PEACE as well as
   its overwhelming powers of DESTRUCTION (see p. 23).
   But as of now, 1960, we have new headaches of course!
   Strontium 90, fall-out, and all the rest.
   Furthermore, even for PEACEFUL uses,
   vital decisions must be made—
   where do we put the radioactive "garbage" which is
   a by-product of even peaceful Atomic Energy plants?!

TO LET THE PEOPLE KNOW
that
NEW TYPE OF THINKING IS ESSENTIAL
IF MANKIND IS TO SURVIVE and
move toward higher levels.
This appeal sent you
only after long consideration
of IMMENSE CRISIS we face.
Urgently request you send
immediate check to me,
as Chairman of
Emergency Committee of
Atomic Scientists,
Princeton, New Jersey.
We ask your help
in this fateful moment.

> (Signed)
> Albert Einstein.

And, believe me, brother,
SAM IS NOT FOOLING!

So,
according to SAM,
the first thing we CAN DO is:
to help the
Modern Paul Revere
to spread the warning of
the World's danger,
by sending money to the *
Emergency Committee
for their
EDUCATIONAL CAMPAIGN
and
by telling all our
friends and neighbors
that
we must

* No longer necessary—see p. 29.

STOP REPEATING
THE OLD SLOGAN that
"There always have been wars,
  there always will be wars"—
for we have reached a point
where

WAR MUST STOP HERE AND NOW!

We must demand that
our representatives in
the Government
understand this and
repeat it until
they
DO SOMETHING about it.
And we MUST NOT
follow any leader who,
like the Goat in
the slaughter houses,
leads the lambs up a ramp,
at the top of which
he is removed to safety,
but the lambs
who trustfully followed him
are slaughtered,
while he starts up again
at the head of a new flock!
And he looks so dignified
and respectable!

Thus the first point in the
NEW TYPE OF THINKING
which we must all learn
is that
we must STOP thinking that

WAR IS INEVITABLE,
and we must replace it by
the MODERN REALISTIC THOUGHT that
WAR MUST BE ELIMINATED
HERE AND NOW,
or we won't live to tell the tale.

Perhaps you are inclined to say:
"But, SAM,
 this may be easy for you,
 but we are only human,
 and much as we would like
 to go along with you
 on this,
 it is impossible for us—
 we are simply not built that way.
After all,
you must understand that
you cannot drive us humans
beyond our strength.
You're a practical fellow
when it comes to
technical things,
but
you don't seem to understand that human beings are
much more complex than
the physical world
and you cannot push us around
even if it is for our own good—
we just can't take it."

IV. OH, YES, YOU CAN TAKE IT!

We are told that
Abraham Lincoln said:
"God must like the common people,
  He made so many of them."
And SAM, too, is very fond of
Mits and Wits,
who are too modest
to know their own strength.
Many of them
surprised themselves
during the war
by doing things
they would have thought to be
impossible.
And SAM knows it
and that is why
he has so much faith in them.
Besides,
as we look back
through the ages,
we see various species
doing the "impossible"
again and again,
adapting themselves
to all sorts of conditions.
Do you think it was
EASY
to grow hands and feet
and brains
and become adapted
to various new environments
through the ages?!—
(as shown on pages 36 and 37)

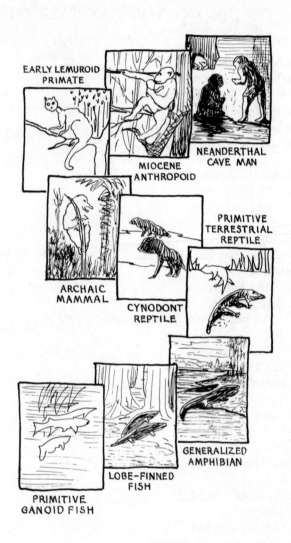

EARLY LEMUROID
PRIMATE

MIOCENE
ANTHROPOID

NEANDERTHAL
CAVE MAN

PRIMITIVE
TERRESTRIAL
REPTILE

ARCHAIC
MAMMAL

CYNODONT
REPTILE

GENERALIZED
AMPHIBIAN

LOBE-FINNED
FISH

PRIMITIVE
GANOID FISH

STUDENTS IN NATURE'S TRAINING SCHOOL

In the present and past ages of the earth Nature has kept a physical and mental training-school of many grades. Her examinations have always been practical ones, the prize of survival being awarded to the "fittest" in each successive grade.

In the primary school the lower grades were passed through under water. Here one learned to swim and steer in the currents, to lurk quietly, to strike successfully. A few grades further on the pupils were equipped with air-sacs, so that they could wriggle out on the banks and use their fore-and-hind paddles as limbs.

After acquiring the physique to withstand hardships of heat and cold, some of the more advanced candidates were admitted to the school of the forests and to the uncertainties of life in the trees, where a practical course in the care and feeding of infants was required of all mothers.

At last the most intelligent pupils ventured out into the open and went into training both for short sprints and cross-country runs. In their manual training schools they learned the art of making flint implements and weapons and with these, before they retired to their dormitories at night, they prepared for themselves their simple meal of bear's meat.

Thus they were trained for the degree of H. S. (Homo sapiens), which was eventually won by their descendants.

(Reprinted by permission of W. K. Gregory and The American Museum of Natural History)

Indeed,
even among plants,
"the same individual plant,
if transplanted,
will take on
a very different form
if grown near a mountain-top
or in a lowland valley;
Ranunculus will acquire
one appropriate shape
if grown in water,
another if grown in air." *

And, of course,
Man's brain,
YOUR brain,
has most miraculous potentialities
for adaptation,
and is certainly
NOT going to permit itself
to be destroyed
just because
it is called upon
to adapt itself to this
NEW, MODERN WORLD.
SAM merely reminds you that
you have done it before and
you CAN DO it again!
Thus,
let us follow SAM's lead
and trace through
the changes in our ideas about
REALISM,
and see how we can apply it
to understand

* See the article on Evolution
  in the *Encyclopaedia Britannica,*
  14th edition.

what IS most REALISTIC
in the modern world
and how the mind can
accept it,
adapt to it,
and reap the usual reward of
adaptation,
namely,
SURVIVAL.

V. REALISM

Take, for example,
an uneducated man,
out in his own back yard,
who sees the sun rise daily,
run its course through the day
and set in the evening.
He naturally thinks
that the sun
revolves around the earth.
His theory is:
"Seeing is believing."
And so,
the occurrences
in the outside world
plus his theory
create in him
a deep FEELING of confidence in
the REALITY of his experience.

Now, after a while,
along come other men,
who not only watch the sun
in its daily course,
but who, like the astronomers,
spend years of their lives
watching the course of
the planets,
and are driven to have
a more sophisticated theory
to explain
the more sophisticated observations—
namely, that
it is the earth

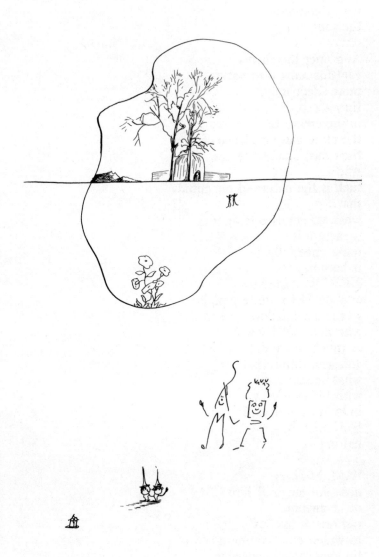

(as well as the other planets)
which goes around
the sun!

And since this theory
explains more observations
more adequately,*
they accept it
in preference to
the more naïve evidence of
their own unaided senses.
And
such is the nature of our minds
that
when we get used to an idea
we accept it
quite cheerfully;
it becomes the
NEW REALISM
and we FEEL quite superior
to the naïve fellow
who does not know
as much as we do,
and who thinks that
what he sees
with his own eyes
in his own back yard
is REALISM—
ha! ha!

SAM, however,
does not laugh at him
or at anyone,
but merely asks us
to widen our "common sense"
through more knowledge.

* See Chapter VII for a
  further discussion of this point.

Thus,
as new instruments
are developed,
telescopes,
microscopes,
spectroscopes,
cyclotrons,
etc., etc.,
more and more observations
are made,
and,
just as before,
the older theories
are less and less able
to account for them
adequately,
and we are driven
by these facts
to develop theories
more sophisticated and
more adequate to
include these facts.
Thus the people who
are right up to date
on the facts of science
and the mathematical theories
which account for them,
have accepted these
as being the new
MODERN REALISM,
far superior to
the naïve realism of
"seeing" and "common sense."
And they FEEL this
modern realism
just as intensely as the less informed person
FEELS and BELIEVES in
his more naïve

observations and theories—
except that
these more sophisticated people
have learned by experience
that this process
of growing sophistication
goes on and on
and they are therefore
not so "set" in their ways
as the more naïve ones,
being more
PREPARED FOR CHANGE
and more willing and able
to make
NECESSARY ADJUSTMENTS
in their ideas about
what is
REALISM!

And so,
SAM,
observing that
these people, these
Scientists,
Artists,
Mathematicians,
have succeeded in
accepting a
NEW REALISM
which fits the world
much better,
and which makes it
possible for them
to ADAPT themselves better,—
thus
SAM knows that
such adaptation is
entirely possible for

44

human beings,
and therefore for
YOU.
And that
all you need for this is
more EDUCATION
of a kind that
will bring you
UP TO DATE on
Science,
Art,
Mathematics,
and then
your own wonderful possession,
your human brain,
will accept this
NEW REALISM
which will help you, too,
to live in this
MODERN WORLD.

Perhaps you are willing
to accept SAM's guidance,
at least in connection with
Science
(which brings in the observations)
and Mathematics
(which helps construct the theories),
but are you wondering
about Art?
How does that fit into the picture?
What does SAM have to do with
MODERN ART?

Well, in the first place
you will agree that
whereas Science gives us
the observations

45

and Mathematics
helps construct the theories,
we need also
to FEEL good about it,
to ACCEPT it
with our intuitive sense of
the fitness of things,
which really belongs to
the domain of Art,
so that
every Scientist
and Mathematician
is, in this sense,
also an Artist.

But, more than this,
the Artist himself
views the world
at first
from his own back yard
and at first
acquires the naïve ideas of
REALISM
according to which
he draws what he "sees,"
houses, people,
landscapes, seascapes,
et al.
But, after a while,
he too becomes aware that
"seeing is believing" and
"common sense"
have to be modified
more and more,
and he finds himself,
in modern times,
just like
the Scientist and Mathematician,

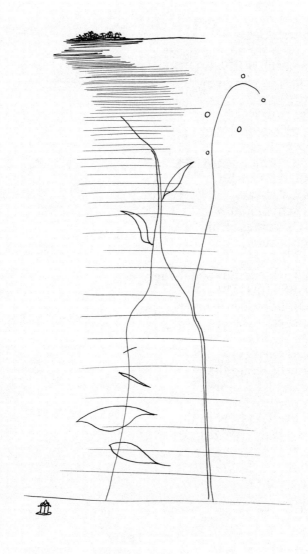

47

tending more and more
toward the
ABSTRACT
as the more adequate kind of
REALISM
needed for adaptation in
the MODERN WORLD.
Thus, in every way,
Art,
the A in SAM,
is an essential part of
his make-up,
and not an isolated part,
but right in his
blood stream
penetrating into
every corner of his
personality.

But what is this about the
"ABSTRACT"?
And how does it function in
Science,
Art,
Mathematics
to help create the
NEW REALISM
so needed for
ADAPTATION to the
MODERN WORLD?

VI. BE PRACTICAL THE MODERN WAY!

And so, apparently,
in order to survive,
the most PRACTICAL thing to do
is to accept
MODERN REALISM,
which implies
becoming familiar with the
ABSTRACT!

This sounds paradoxical to the NAÏVE mind,
but when we fully realize
that this is the only way to
SURVIVE,
we shall find
not only that we can
take it
all right,
but that it is such
FUN
to be SOPHISTICATED!

But
how is it possible
to become
sufficiently up to date in
Science,
Art,
Mathematics
to really appreciate their
MODERN REALISM and
to use it for our own
SURVIVAL and PLEASURE?
These are such vast domains!

Therefore SAM suggests
a twofold program:

(1) An EMERGENCY program:

    (a) To heed the
        WARNING of the
        MODERN PAUL REVERE,
        even if it means that
        we must get up from
        our nice warm beds
        and come to the rescue of
        not only America
        but the whole world by
        PREVENTING WAR,
        DEMANDING an
        INTERNATIONAL police force,
        DISARMAMENT of ALL NATIONS,
        (to include ALL the horrible
        modern weapons),
        and whatever
        SAM
        recommends! *
        Thus we can gain
        the time needed for
        the longer process of
        EDUCATION for the
        MODERN WORLD
        which SAM advocates.

    (b) To follow SAM's advice
        and nobody else's,
        even if we cannot yet
        quite understand
        all his reasons.

* You can subscribe to the
Bulletin of the Atomic Scientists
and keep yourself informed.

For he is our best friend!
He is trying so hard
to reach us.
We MUST keep ourselves
informed of his doings
and NOT follow
any of the Goats
up the ramp
to our DOOM
like the poor lambs in
the slaughterhouses!

(2) A long-term program of
EDUCATION,
starting in early youth
and continuing
as long as we live,
to become really acquainted
with SAM,
our best friend and guide.
For he will bring us
peace,
knowledge of
the world we live in,
the means to adapt ourselves
to this world,
resulting in
peace of mind,
plenty and
happiness.
For we must remember that
working for SAM,
to accomplish all these things,
are those who
can find
the peaceful uses of

atomic energy—
to cure disease,
to make food "out of the air"
(by photosynthesis),
to give us each
a home and garden,
to lengthen
youthful healthful life,
to think straight,
to have fun in
so many ways that
we can hardly imagine it!

And who stands in the way
of SAM's program?
Why, the ANTI–SAM–ITES of course!
Those who want to lead us
to believe that
World War III is inevitable,
who make us spend
most of our time and energy
and money
in preparing again
to destroy each other,
those who believe that
different races
must hate each other,
those who contradict
SAM's six-point warning!
Please refresh your memory on
these six points (page 20)
so that you can
not only
follow them yourself,
but help spread them,
and especially use them
as a means of recognizing
who ARE the Goats

leading us lambs
to the slaughter!

It is really a battle between
SAM's MEN and
the Goats,
and it is up to
Mits and Wits to
HELP SAM to
HELP MITS and WITS.

And now
let us ask SAM
to give us some idea of
ABSTRACT
MODERN
REALISM.

PART II

REALISM—MODERN STYLE

VII. MODERN REALISM IN SCIENCE

Even a naïve person
should admit that
"seeing is believing" is
rather a crude guide to
Reality,
for, after all, if
you see "pink elephants"
or hear "voices"
which no one else
sees or hears,
you would hardly call
these hallucinations
Reality!

Or,
if you look at an object
and see something like this:

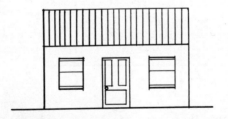

you may be seeing a house,
or perhaps just a billboard,
and it is not until
you look at it from
other points of view
that you can decide whether
it is a real house or not.

Thus you will agree that
a good way to describe
a "real" thing is
that which remains
INVARIANT
from different viewpoints,
or,
as a Scientist prefers to say:
INVARIANT under a given
TRANSFORMATION of axes.
For instance:

Suppose we are interested in
the distance from
A to B
and cannot measure it
directly,
because of some obstruction,
as shown:

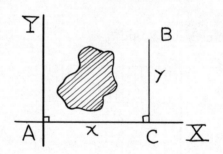

And suppose that
an ingenious gentleman,
Mr. K by name,
suggests the following:
Draw two lines, AX and AY,
perpendicular to each other,
and then draw
BC perpendicular to AX.

Then the distance from A to B
(call it d)
can be found by measuring x and y
and then calculating d,
by means of the well-known
Pythagorean Theorem:

$$d = \sqrt{x^2 + y^2}$$

Suppose, further,
that another gentleman,
Mr. K',
equally ingenious,
suggests a similar method
but uses a different pair of
rectangular axes,
AX' and AY':

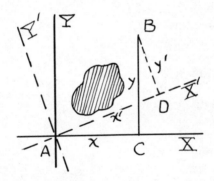

He therefore measures
x' (= AD) and y' (= BD)
instead of x and y as K did,
and yet,
by means of the
Pythagorean Theorem,
he too can calculate d by

$$d = \sqrt{(x')^2 + (y')^2}$$

Thus d is an
INVARIANT
under a ROTATION of the axes,
and therefore represents
what is "real" to
both K and K',
as against
the abscissa (x and x') and
the ordinate (y and y')
on which they do NOT agree.
Thus in Science
two observers,
K and K',
EMPHASIZE the INVARIANTS,
the "REALITY"
(in this case,
the distance between two points),
upon which they AGREE,
while, at the same time,
each allows the other
to have his own way in
measuring the
abscissa and ordinate,
agreeing to disagree on
these matters,
so long as they have
some common ground
where they can
do business together!
Is there not
a moral here
for human relations?

Similarly,
if the issue is
the distance between two points
in THREE dimensions,
you probably know that

the formula needed here is

$$d = \sqrt{x^2 + y^2 + z^2}$$

and

$$\sqrt{x^2 + y^2 + z^2} = \sqrt{(x')^2 + (y')^2 + (z')^2}$$

that is,
the distance between two points
is again an
INVARIANT
under a rotation of
the three axes.
It is important to note,
however,
that in three dimensions
$\sqrt{x^2 + y^2}\,(= AC)$ represents
merely the "shadow" of d
upon the XY plane,
as shown in the following diagram:

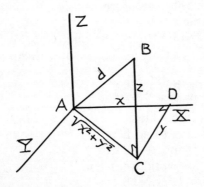

Hence, in this case, we have:

K and K′ AGREE on:

(1) the LENGTH of an object (d).
(2) The use of the Pythagorean Theorem.

K and K' agree to DISAGREE on:

(1) the 3 co-ordinates:

$$x \neq x'$$
$$y \neq y'$$
$$z \neq z'$$

(2) the "SHADOW" of d:

$$\sqrt{x^2 + y^2} \neq \sqrt{(x')^2 + (y')^2}$$

since the shadow
changes in length
as the object, d,
changes its inclination
relatively to the 3 axes.
Thus the "shadow"
is NOT a "REALITY."

And so, again,
K and K' have their
INVARIANTS,
their "REALITY,"
upon which they can agree
and do business,
while frankly admitting their differences,
WITHOUT starting a FIGHT over them!
And now,
let us see how this applies
in Modern Physics.
For reasons into which
it in inadvisable to go here,*
it has been found to be wise
to consider the world we live in
as a world of EVENTS,
instead of
a three-dimensional SPACE of

* See "The Einstein Theory of Relativity"
by Lillian R. Lieber,
with drawings by Hugh Gray Lieber
(Rinehart & Co., 1945)

62

POINTS,
with TIME coming in as
a separate consideration.
Now, to specify a certain event,
one would have to tell
the time and place of
its occurrence;
and since
it takes three numbers
to specify the place
(latitude, x, longitude, y, and altitude, z)
and one number for the time,
it thus takes in all
FOUR NUMBERS
to specify an event,
and therefore we may say that
the world of EVENTS
is FOUR-dimensional,
and hence,
in this sense,
we actually live in a
FOUR–DIMENSIONAL WORLD.
And, under a certain
rotation of axes,
the INVARIANT here is

$$d = \sqrt{x^2 + y^2 + z^2 + \tau^2}$$

where τ is related to the TIME
and where d is
the "space-time interval"
between two events
(instead of
the distance between 2 points,
as before);
and thus we now have:

K and K' AGREE on:

$$d = \sqrt{x^2 + y^2 + z^2 + \tau^2}$$

K and K' agree to DISAGREE on:

(1)
$$x \neq x'$$
$$y \neq y'$$
$$z \neq z'$$
$$\tau \neq \tau'$$

(2) $\sqrt{x^2 + y^2} \neq \sqrt{(x')^2 + (y')^2}$

(3) $\sqrt{x^2 + y^2 + z^2} \neq \sqrt{(x')^2 + (y')^2 + (z')^2}$

Thus,
in our modern
FOUR–DIMENSIONAL
SPACE–TIME WORLD of EVENTS,
the length of an object
(namely $\sqrt{x^2 + y^2 + z^2}$)
is NOT an INVARIANT,
but is more like a "shadow";
whereas
the more ABSTRACT concept,
namely,
the SPACE–TIME INTERVAL
between two EVENTS,
is now the INVARIANT or
REALITY!
Thus the things
(like the length of an object)
which seem so real
to the naïve person
are NOT "real"
when all the data
are taken into account,
and the LESS OBVIOUS things
(like the space-time interval between two events)
become more "real." †

† If this sounds a little "mystical" to you,
look it up in the book mentioned on p. 62,
where it is clearly explained.

64

Thus we see that
MODERN REALISM,
which is BASED on
a vast amount of EXPERIMENTAL data,
leads us
(1) to accept
ABSTRACT concepts
as the more adequate
REALITY
and
(2) to accept these
in spite of
the differences which exist
(and are freely acknowledged)
between observers
having different viewpoints
(or co-ordinate systems).
This is how
the SOPHISTICATED HUMAN MIND
deals SUCCESSFULLY with
the complications of
the modern world.

Does it not behoove us
also in social relations
to find those basic
INVARIANTS (REALITIES)
like the
(1) DESIRE FOR PEACE
(2) NEED of FOOD and SHELTER
(3) Necessity of ELIMINATION of ALL
WEAPONS of
MASS DESTRUCTION
(4) CRAVING for JUSTICE and
HUMAN DIGNITY,
etc.,
the REALITIES for ALL NATIONS,
and to do business with

each other,
while agreeing to
let each one be
DIFFERENT in
language, customs, music, etc.,—
differences which,
if accepted,
will add color and variety
and enjoyment
to all our lives,
instead of being
a source of strife!
If anyone claims that
it is impossible for
the human mind
to adjust itself
to such an idea,
let him remember that in
MODERN PHYSICS
the human mind
has been able to accept
the seemingly fantastic ideas
that
things we actually see
are mere SHADOWS,
and that things which are
ABSTRACT,
like the
"space-time interval
between two events,"
or the ATOM
(which has never been seen or
even pictured by anyone)
are the REALITIES of the
MODERN WORLD!

These ideas were
NOT EASY to accept,

but your wonderful
human mind
CAN DO it.
Let no one claim that
he cannot accept the
NECESSARY ideas for
ALL NATIONS
to live together in
PEACE
on this ONE EARTH
without first
MAKING THE GREAT EFFORT
that
the Scientists have made
in accepting
the fantastic ideas of
modern science.
And, indeed,
when the resistance stops
the mind becomes
happier than ever
because it is then
so much better adjusted to
the modern environment,
and is then in contact
with the complexity of
the modern world
without being confused by it!

It is not the ABSTRACT that
the mind really dreads,
but rather the confusion
which comes from being
TOO NAÏVE!

VIII. CAN WE BE HAPPY WITH SAM?

Are you thinking that
if life is to be so difficult,
is the game worth the candle?

But if you examine SAM's personality
carefully,
you will find that
the A in SAM,
which is in his very heart,
and which is
the essence of life,
DEMANDS that
life bring "happiness."
Let us examine this remark
to see what it means.
The meaning of "happiness,"
as used here,
is:
the sense of joy which
an individual feels
at the moment when
he "unites" with
some other individual,
whether this latter is
another human being
(in love or friendship),
or a house
or a picture
or a tune
or an idea
or anything.
This intense desire
for union

is at the basis of
the "religious experience,"
of the desire for
ONE God,
for ONE theory embracing
the entire universe.
It may be called
"the aesthetic principle."
It is the basis
for the desire
to "smooth out"
the physical world
(which is made up of
discrete "quanta"),
thus resulting in the concept of
"continuity."
It makes us see
a "continuous" moving picture
even though we know
it is made up of
a series of
separate individual pictures.
It makes us want to
"glide,"
to dance,
to do anything which
gives this sense of
"smoothness" and "union" and
"oneness."
It is the essence of
happiness and life.

Now if you will accept
this lengthy description
of the A in SAM,
you will agree that
SAM wants you
to live and be happy,

and has an
enormous variety of ways
of being happy—
anywhere from
"swing" to
"religion,"
from skiing to
abstract mathematics,
anything with which
you can "unite."

Now,
suppose you grant this
for a moment,
and then ask:
"But is this 'happiness,'
  this variety of ways of
  'uniting' with others,
  this 'smoothing out'
  of the discrete into
  the continuous—
  is it good for us?"
And you will surely agree
that it depends on
WHAT you unite with,
and on
HOW MUCH uniting you do.
For instance,
if you "unite" with food,
it sustains your life
for you have
the magic ability
to transform the food into
YOU;
each one of us,
eating the same food,
magically converts it
into his own personality.

You are a magician
and you don't realize it!
But obviously
this need for food
can lead us astray,
a child must be guided away
from eating harmful things,
and even many adults
(gourmands and drunkards)
eat and drink
either harmful things
or more than they should,
thus allowing their
basic desire
to "unite" with food,
to mislead them.
Thus Hollywood and
your physician and
the insurance companies
all try to check
this desire to "eat"
and tell us where to stop.

Similarly,
the desire to "unite"
with material things,
to possess wealth,
goes on and on in some people,
until they want to
gather unto themselves
earthly possessions
not only beyond their own needs
but actually
to their own detriment.
Can Hollywood and
the psychiatrists
help SAM
by encouraging us

to put a wise limit on
the desire to "unite"
in this direction also?
Even in skiing
you have to watch out
for the trees,
and not give free rein
to the intense desire
to "glide,"
without caution.

If, then,
we are blessed with
this great desire
for "happiness"
and if it needs
curbing
to prevent us from
destroying ourselves,
what are we to do about it?
Well, SAM says
that we are lucky
in having
so many different ways
of achieving this "happiness"—
we do not have to
eat so much that we get
fatty degeneration,
or drink until we get
the D.T.'s,
or accumulate wealth until
we become overwhelmed
with our own greed.
For we can also
"unite"
with ideas!
Here, too, however,
we must carefully

73

"select" the ideas,
for some of them
are poison, too,
and can destroy us.
But we are still far from
having too many good ideas.
We are not yet
TOO fat with GOOD ideas,
which lead to
LIFE instead of death!
In the domain of ideas
we are still suffering from
malnutrition,
because we have been fed
too many poisonous ideas which
lead to
death and destruction.
Thus we have much "uniting" to do
in the immediate future,
to form the
"United Nations"
to make
"One World,"
to "join up" with
SAM
for peace and plenty
and happiness
for all.
For SAM can help us
to SELECT
the right kind and amount of
"food"
for our bodies and minds—
through his staff of
biologists,
physicians,
psychiatrists,—
indeed, all

Scientists,
Artists,
Mathematicians.
OUR job is
to "unite" with
all this knowledge,
not only because
we need SAM's guidance
to go toward
LIFE instead of death,
but,
this very act of
"uniting" with knowledge
will bring us
the very "happiness" we seek!
But, SAM reminds us,
this "happiness" itself
is NOT continuous
but comes in moments,
and between these moments
there is work to be done,
just as
in climbing a mountain,
the moments when we stop
to "unite" with the landscape
are intermittent,
each being followed by
further effort
to reach
a still "more beautiful" view,
with which we again
"unite" for a moment.

And so
let us follow SAM
a little way up
Mt. Mathematics
to see how the

75

ABSTRACT
can help us.
And if we "unite" with it
and let the magic of our minds
convert it into
our own personalities
(as we do with food),
we shall derive
both pleasure and profit
(as we do from food).

IX. A NEW VIEW FROM MT. MATH

As we saw in Chapter VII,
even in Science, which is
our closest contact with
the outside world,
modern "REALITIES"
are ABSTRACT!
And,
not only have we been
driven to this by
the EXPERIMENTAL data,
but we saw in Chapter VIII
that this is FORTUNATE
because
in the domain of IDEAS
there are
many opportunities
for satisfying
that aesthetic urge for
"union"
after having reached
a wholesome limit in
"union" on the
more naïve, physical level
(food, drink, etc.).
Of course
for those who do NOT YET
have enough food, etc.,
this craving comes first
and must be satisfied first—
and if those who do have enough
of these things
will "unite" with this "idea"
they will find "happiness"

in feeding the others.
But, in addition to that,
we need a domain for
"union"
in which there seems to be
no limit for "happiness"—
and that is
the ABSTRACT.

Thus let us try
to get a glimpse of
what has been done
in this respect in
Mathematics,
and see how it can help us.

We all know
from ordinary arithmetic
that
in multiplying two numbers
(say 7 and 11)
it does not matter which number
is written first:
thus $7 \times 11 = 77$ and
also $11 \times 7 = 77$,
giving us the same answer
either way.
Expressing this basic rule of
arithmetic
in more general terms,
as is done in algebra,
we write
$$a \times b = b \times a,$$
showing that this rule applies
for any pair of numbers
(not just 7 and 11).
Thus in going from
arithmetic to

algebra,
we find that
we gain in GENERALITY,
obtaining a relationship
$$a \times b = b \times a,$$
which then applies to
more cases than just
$$7 \times 11 = 11 \times 7.$$
Indeed,
when you stop to think of it,
even writing a number, like 7,
is already
more "abstract" than
"7 apples,"
which refers to concrete objects.
Thus, a child,
in learning arithmetic,
must first start
with actual concrete objects
to appreciate the meaning of
"addition," for instance.
Gradually, however,
he accepts the idea of
working with
the numbers themselves,
and,
later on, in algebra,
he abstracts still further
and learns to use
letters instead of numbers.

And please note that
each time
we go further into
the abstract
we GAIN in GENERALITY,
which makes the result
applicable to more cases

and therefore
MORE practical, NOT LESS!

But arithmetic and algebra
are of course
by this time
an old story.
For in MODERN mathematics
this process of
abstraction
has been going on and on,
with the result that
now
the letters need not even
represent numbers at all,
but may represent
ANY kind of "elements,"
and the word
MULTIPLICATION
need not represent
our old familiar friend in
arithmetic
(as in 7×11),
but may now mean
ANY "operation."
For instance,
suppose that
a and b represent "events,"
and suppose we take
multiplication to mean
"is followed by,"
then $a \times b$ would mean
that some event, a,
say, being born,
is followed by
some other event, b,
say, being married.
Now notice that

here
$a \times b$
does NOT equal
$b \times a$;
thus

$$a \times b \neq b \times a$$

under this interpretation
of a, b, and $\times$;
and thus
the old familiar
COMMUTATIVE LAW of MULTIPLICATION
(namely $a \times b = b \times a$),
which is so familiar to us in
arithmetic and algebra,
does NOT hold here.
Well, you might say,
so what is the use of it?
Is it not just going to
confuse us
after we have taken
so much trouble to learn
arithmetic and algebra?

NOT AT ALL!

For
all one needs to do
to keep from being confused
is to SPECIFY
the interpretation,
as on page 81,
and we then know that
we are not speaking of
ordinary arithmetic or algebra
but of some other domain
which makes just as much
SENSE,
but has DIFFERENT basic rules.

Thus we gain the
ADVANTAGE
OF BEING ABLE TO PUT
THE WONDERFUL MATHEMATICAL
SYMBOLISM
to NEW and IMPORTANT
USES,*
since arithmetic and algebra,
useful as they are,
are NOT adequate for
tackling the great VARIETY of
situations which we meet in life.
Later,
in Part III,
you will see how
a NEW "algebra,"
whose basic rules are
different from those
of our ordinary algebra,
is most useful in
LOGIC,
which we need
not only in
Mathematics and Science
but in ALL thinking
in our daily living!

And so you see
that
excursions into the
ABSTRACT,
far from being impractical,
are,
on the contrary,

* For instance, see
  "Theory of Games and Economic Behavior" by
  von Neumann and Morgenstern
  (Princeton University Press, 1944).

most rewarding in
giving us results
which can be applied
to more and more cases
and therefore become
more and more
USEFUL
to
more and more
PEOPLE
in more and more
SITUATIONS
we meet in life—
not just a device which
helps an accountant
to figure your income tax,
important as that may be.

Thus
the explorers of the
ABSTRACT in
Mathematics
have brought back to us
MANY
"arithmetics,"
"algebras,"
"geometries"
which are applicable
in LOGIC
(needed in ALL thinking),
in NON–EUCLIDEAN GEOMETRIES
(needed in MODERN PHYSICS),
in the THEORY of GROUPS
(valuable in the
Theory of Equations
so basic in ordinary algebra),
etc., etc., etc.
They have discovered

a veritable
TREASURE HOUSE,
with UNLIMITED treasure,
enough for all of us
to "unite" with,
without depriving anyone else
of his share!

X. THE ABSTRACT IN ART

Thus we have seen that,
in Science,
the ABSTRACT
is more REALISTIC
than the superficial
so-called realism of the
local yokel,
and that it has become
ESSENTIAL
in adapting our minds
to the experimental facts
of the physical world,
and is therefore most
PRACTICAL!

And,
in Mathematics,
the ABSTRACT
has enriched us
with so many new fields,
which have so many
NEW applications,
and so many more possibilities of
PRACTICAL applications
than ever before.

And now
let us take a look at
the ABSTRACT
in Art.
Here again
the naïve, unsophisticated
artist who

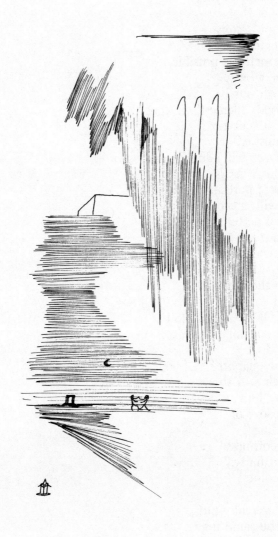

wishes to make
a portrait of you,
thinks that
he must copy
your features
as exactly as possible,
otherwise
it will not be
a good "likeness" of you,
it will not be
"realistic."
But you will admit that
if the artist is
a great portrait painter,
he will expect
to do better than that,
to put your "character"
(which is more "abstract"
than your face)
into the portrait.
And
a MODERN ARTIST
will go still further
and do
a "psyquaport" * of you,
which will show
your "human-ness,"
your love of
"gliding,"
"smoothness,"
"continuity,"
"happiness,"
"life,"
all different words
for the same urge

* A word invented by
  Hugh Gray Lieber
  to describe the drawings he makes.

to "unite" yourself
with all the world,
physical and mental.
The result is
an "abstract" portrait of you,
a "psyquaport,"
which,
by virtue of its
GENERAL human-ness,
is then a portrait
not of you alone,
but of all humanity,
and has therefore
more of the quality of
universality
than does a mere
snapshot of
your physical self.
Hence a psyquaport
appeals to many people,
who see in it also
their own "human-ness,"
just as
a symphony has
a more UNIVERSAL appeal
(to the sophisticated)
than a song with words,
which tells a concrete story
and which therefore
appeals to
the more naïve person.

And so we see that
the concrete objects,
the superficial "realities,"
the "common sense" of
the naïve, uninformed person,
have all given way

to more abstract
and deeper "realities"
of the modern world
in all domains.

We CAN and MUST
adapt ourselves to
this modern world,
and learn to
"unite" with the "abstract"
in order to
"live" and be "happy" in it.
And so,
in looking at
the psyquaports
on the next few pages,
do not look for
snapshots of concrete objects,
but look for
something to "unite" with,
to "enjoy,"
to "eat,"
to "absorb" into yourself,—
whether it be
grace of curve
or some associations
of your own,
or ideas,
or what have you.
It is like listening to
a symphony—
feel free to
think your own thoughts,
to make your own
applications to
your own needs—
just as
various scientists

make their own applications
to their own needs
of abstract mathematics.

That is why
a modern artist
does not, as a rule,
give names to his pictures.
And when he does,
he often gives them
different names at
different times,
showing that
they do not have
specific definite meanings
even for the artist himself—
any more than
Abstract Mathematics has for
the mathematician himself,
until it is "applied."

You may be interested
to know that
these psyquaports
are not sketched out first
but come "gliding" out of
the artist,
like oil out of a well,
or water in a stream,
without any effort—
a truly NATURAL phenomenon,
wonderful to behold!
You would probably
enjoy them even more
if you could see them
in the process,
as you watch
an expert dancer

or skier,
or listen to a great violinist.

And now look at
these drawings
and see if you can
find in them
something of
the magic
and beauty
of YOUR OWN
human spirit.†

† See also the book of drawings:
  "Good-bye Mr. Man, Hello Mr. NEWman"
  by Hugh Gray Lieber,
  with an Introduction by
  Lillian R. Lieber
  (Galois Institute Press, 1958).

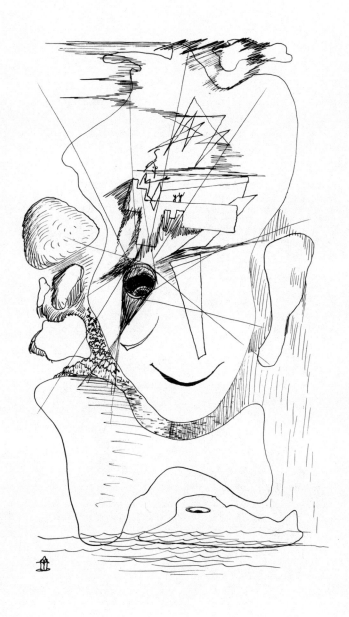

93

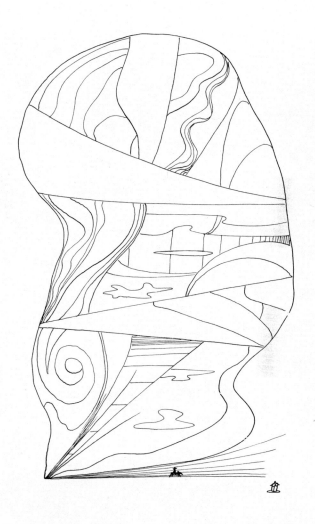

LOGIC

XI. THANK YOU, SAM!

Thus we see that:

(1) SAM is much more
POWERFUL and IMAGINATIVE
than "Superman" or
"Mighty Mouse,"
for he has all the
Scientists and Mathematicians
working for him
to help us,—
if we would only
avail ourselves of
all their wonderful inventions,
now ready for us,
and more to come!

(2) He is much more
KIND than "Robin Hood"
for he does not have to
rob one to pay another,
but has
ABUNDANCE for EVERYONE!

(3) He is much more
SANE than
a "Fairy Godmother,"
for she is only
an "escape mechanism,"
whereas he is a
REALISTIC IDEALIST!

(4) He agrees with
the great RELIGIONS,
which have long been telling us:
Thou shalt not kill.

(SAM too is for LIFE, against death!)
Thou shalt not steal
(no need to,
he has abundance for all).
And so on and so on.

(5) He is HONEST,
    he will never double-cross you.

(6) He preaches love
    (remember the A in SAM?)

Although he advocates
"uniting" with all the world
into ONE SOCIETY,
he does not forget
the need for "happiness" of
each INDIVIDUAL.
He is thus
for liberty and justice for all
regardless of race, creed or color.
He is for democracy
and can give us
some good, CLEAR ideas
about it.
For instance:
there is Freedom of Speech in
Science,
but freedom to say what?
Why, obviously,
to say something
INTELLIGENT and CONSTRUCTIVE,
not merely to heckle
or just to make a noise.
Similarly,
in considering VARIOUS issues
we can learn to ask
"What would SAM say about this,
  or what would SAM do about that?"

It is surprising how,
when we form this habit,
he actually comes to the rescue
with excellent advice.

Try it and see!

For instance,
let us ask SAM about
LOGIC:
(1) What IS Logic?
(2) What is traditional,
    Aristotelian Logic?
(3) What is
    modern, streamlined Logic?
(4) How can it be of
    USE to us ALL?

XII. WHAT IS LOGIC?

One day
the following incident took place:
A high-school boy,
who had studied
Euclidean plane geometry,
and the school janitor, who
had once been a seaman,
were having an "argument"
about the shortest path
from New York to Paris.
The boy,
maintaining that
"A straight line is
 the shortest distance between
 two points,"
placed a ruler on the map
and drew a straight line
between New York and Paris,
claiming that
this is the shortest path.
The former sailor, however,
maintained that
the shortest path would be
along a curve!
And so the boy said:
"The trouble with you is
 that you never
 studied geometry,
 and therefore
 you make statements that
 are not logical!"

Now, as a matter of fact,
the sailor was right
and the high-school boy wrong.
But please do not
jump to the conclusion
that it is wrong to
study geometry!
The point is that
if the boy had known
MORE geometry
he would have agreed
with the sailor,
who picked up
this information from
his practical experience
but,
not having had
a good education,
was unable to
defend himself,
and so they argued and argued
without getting anywhere!
The fact is that
BOTH
education and experience—
and plenty of each—
are needed.

Now let us examine
what the fight was all about.

You will agree that
if you cut the surface
of a globe in half
along a meridian
and tried to lay one half
flat on the table,
it just would not lie flat,

but would look like a cup—
unless you stretched it
at the North and South poles,
stretching each of these points
into a line as long as
the equator.
Now, in doing so,
you would distort
the regions around the poles,
so that
on such a flat map
Greenland appears to be
the same size as
South America,
whereas
on the globe
you can easily see that
Greenland is really
very much smaller than
South America!
Similarly,
to get some idea of
the shortest path
from New York to Paris,
stretch a string right on
the globe,
between these cities,
and you will see that
the path goes through
Newfoundland and Ireland,
which does NOT agree
with the straight-line path
on your flat map!
Thus the sailor knew this
from experience,
whereas the boy
did not realize that
the geometry on

the surface of a sphere
is DIFFERENT from the
Euclidean Geometry which
he had studied.*

Nowadays,
with fast airplane travel
coming in,
we are becoming
more "globe"-conscious,
and therefore should be
more map-conscious,
realizing that
different maps are useful for
different purposes.†

But where does
the "logic" come in?

Well,
if you make a SINGLE statement,
it makes no sense to say
that it is either
"logical" or "illogical";
it is only when
from one statement
you "infer" a second one
(you "draw a conclusion"),
that you can call
the process
"logical" or "illogical":

* See "Non-Euclidean Geometry"
  by Lillian R. Lieber
  with drawings by
  Hugh Gray Lieber
  (Galois Institute Press, 4th printing, 1959).
† See "Military and Naval Maps and
  Grids" by W. W. Flexner and G. L. Walker
  (Dryden Press, 1942).

it is "logical" when
your conclusion is drawn
VALIDLY,
and "illogical" when
your conclusion is
NOT VALIDLY drawn;
in the latter case
the conclusion is sometimes
referred to by the Latin term
"non sequitur," which means
it does NOT FOLLOW
from your first statement
(called the "premise").
Thus our young friend (page 104)
was really being illogical, for
from the premise of having
a non-Euclidean surface (the globe)
he was falsely drawing
Euclidean conclusions
which do NOT FOLLOW for
the surface of the earth!

You have probably heard lawyers
use the term
"non sequitur,"
for, in their experience,
they often find
people being "illogical."
A common example of
a DANGEROUS non sequitur is:
(1) Your religion is
    different from mine. (Premise)
(2) Therefore you are no good! (Conclusion)

Thus lawyers and judges,
in order to serve justice,
are obliged to rule out
non sequiturs—

these are considered
a "foul"
in an argument.
And you can see that
all of us,
even outside of law courts,
should be obliged
to rule out
such "foul" arguments
if we want more
justice and peace,
so that we can all have a chance
to tackle
the ever-present problem of
adaptation to the modern world
and thus reap the benefit in
survival and happiness.
This will be hard enough to do
if we all work together,
but impossible for ANYONE
if we use up our strength
in getting "tough" with
each other, instead of
getting "tough" with
the PROBLEM itself!

A simple illustration of
a VALID conclusion is:

(1) From the premise:
    "If people live in
    New York State,
    they live in the
    United States of America"

(2) you can safely CONCLUDE:
    "Therefore
    if they do NOT live in the

United States of America
then they certainly
do NOT live in
New York State."

From the following diagram
you can easily see that
these two statements
are really saying
the SAME thing
using slightly different wording.

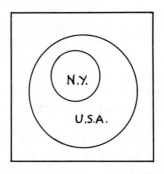

Since the circle representing
the N. Y. State dwellers
is entirely enclosed in
the larger, U.S.A., circle,
then it AUTOMATICALLY follows
that all those
outside of the larger circle
are certainly outside of
the smaller circle.

Such a simple inference
which follows directly
from a premise
without the mediation of
any other statement

is called an
"immediate" inference.
But more often
reasoning is not as simple
as this.
A common type of reasoning is
the "mediate" inference,
which requires a "middle" statement
before the conclusion can be drawn.
An example of this type is
the so-called
SYLLOGISM,
the study of which
dates way back to
Aristotle,
and is known as
Aristotelian Logic or
Traditional Logic.
It is still treated in most
college courses and texts,
although it is now known to be
only a very small part of
Modern Symbolic Logic,
which has become
a wonderful streamlined
mathematical machine,
but which has not yet replaced
the traditional methods
in many colleges!

Let us first take a look
at the old way,
so that you can better
appreciate
the "modern improvements."

XIII. ARISTOTLE AND BARBARA

Thus we see that
Logic is
the study of
HOW TO DRAW CONCLUSIONS VALIDLY.
As was stated at the end of
Chapter XII,
Traditional Logic,
though now known to be
only a tiny part of
Modern Logic,
is still studied in the old way,
and therefore
you may be interested to
get a glimpse of it
so you can somewhat appreciate
the following quotation: *

"Thousands of men,
  through thousands of years,
  have had millions of headaches
  over the valid and invalid
  combinations of these terms,
  arranging, relating and
  naming them.
  Symbolic Logic proves them all
  equivalent to
  just three forms of a
  much greater system."

* See p. 355, "Introduction to Symbolic
  Logic" by S. K. Langer
  (Houghton Mifflin Co., 1937).

113

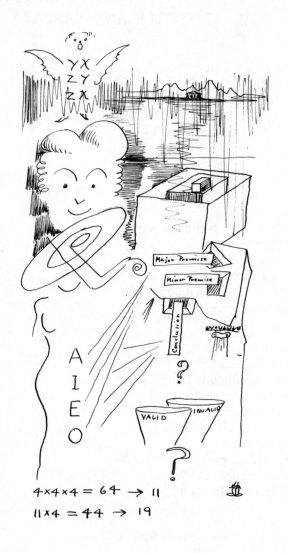

$$4 \times 4 \times 4 = 64 \rightarrow 11$$

$$11 \times 4 = 44 \rightarrow 19$$

Let us therefore proceed
to the study of
SYLLOGISMS:

A syllogism consists of
three and only three propositions:

(1) the major premise
(2) the minor premise
(3) the conclusion.

And the problem in the old
Aristotelian Logic was
to determine what must be
the GENERAL form (or forms)
of the two premises
in order that
the conclusion may be
validly drawn,
thus giving us a kind of
"thought-machine"
to help us to draw conclusions
VALIDLY,
and not jump at
non sequiturs
which are based on
mere personal prejudices,
mere "wishful thinking."

You must admit that
it took a great man
to conceive such an idea,
even if it does need
streamlining today.

Now an "argument" often
consists of a SERIES of
syllogisms,
not very clearly or completely

115

stated.
And it then behooves us
to clarify and complete them,
and then to test their validity
by Aristotelian Logic
(preferably, of course, using
the new symbolism,
which you will see in
subsequent chapters).

Let us therefore return to
the consideration of
the syllogism.

Each proposition of a syllogism
consists of two terms,
subject and predicate
(connected by a verb),
such that
there are only three distinct terms in
the entire syllogism,
each term therefore
occurring twice in
the syllogism.
For instance:
the following is a syllogism:

(1) All metals † are elements.
    (Major premise)
(2) All iron is metal. (Minor premise)
(3) Therefore iron is an element. (Conclusion)

† "Metal," as used here,
  is a technical term,
  as used in Chemistry,
  and not as used
  colloquially
  to include alloys,
  which are not "elements."

Here the terms are:
iron, metal, element.
Note that
each occurs twice in the
syllogism,
and the "middle" term
(metal, in this case)
does NOT occur in the conclusion.

Note further that
a proposition may be

(1) UNIVERSAL
    (if it applies to
    ALL members of a class,
    like
    "ALL metals are elements")

or

(2) PARTICULAR
    (if it applies to only
    SOME members of a class,
    like
    "SOME men are trustworthy.")
Also a proposition may be
AFFIRMATIVE or NEGATIVE.

Thus propositions may be
of four different kinds:

(1) UNIVERSAL AFFIRMATIVE   (A)
(2) UNIVERSAL NEGATIVE   (E)
(3) PARTICULAR AFFIRMATIVE   (I)
(4) PARTICULAR NEGATIVE   (O)

Notice that the letters A and I
occur in the Latin word
"affirmo"
and E and O occur in

"nego."
This helps to remember
which is which.

Now, since a syllogism
contains three propositions,
and since each of these may be
one of four kinds (A, E, I, O)
we can form
$4 \times 4 \times 4$ or 64
different kinds of syllogisms,
called "Moods."
Thus the syllogism on page 116
may be represented by
AAA.

Now
these 64 different "Moods"
are by no means all valid!
Indeed there are
RULES of validity: ‡

(1) The middle term must be
distributed once at least
(i.e., the whole of it
must be referred to
universally
in one premise, if not both).
(2) No term must be
distributed in the conclusion
which was not distributed in
one of the premises.
(3) From two negative premises
nothing can be inferred.
(4) If one premise be negative,
the conclusion must be negative;
and vice versa:

‡ See any standard book on Traditional Logic.

to prove a negative conclusion
one of the premises must be
negative.

(5) From two particular premises
no conclusion can be drawn.

(6) If one premise be particular,
the conclusion must be
particular.

You may wish to try your hand
at using these rules
in order to select from
the 64 possible Moods
mentioned above,
those which are valid.
In order to do this,
it will help you
to write out
the 64 cases
in a systematic manner,
thus:

(1) AAA	(5) AEA	(9) AIA	(13) AOA
(2) AAE	(6) AEE	(10) AIE	(14) AOE
(3) AAI	(7) AEI	(11) AII	(15) AOI
(4) AAO	(8) AEO	(12) AIO	(16) AOO

etc.
The next 16 cases will of course
all have E down the
first column;
then the second column will have
A's in the first four
E's in the next four,
etc.,
and the third column will have
AEIO in each set.
Similarly,
the next 16 will have

all *I*'s in the first column,
etc.,
and the last batch of 16
will have all *O*'s in
the first column, etc.,
thus making 64 cases
in all.

You will now see that
some of the 64 Moods
do not satisfy the rules on pages 118 and 119.
Thus, *AIA* is not valid
according to rule (6),
which says that
if one premise be particular
(*I*, the minor premise, here),
the conclusion must be particular
(whereas here, the conclusion, *A*,
is universal).
Similarly show that
EEI, *IEA*, *IOI*, etc.,
are not valid.
If you examine all the 64,
you will find that
only 11 valid ones remain.

But this is not all!
For, in addition to Moods,
there are also
"Figures,"
four "Figures,"
and each Mood may be
expressed in each of the four
Figures,
so that we have
$11 \times 4 = 44$ possible forms.
To understand what is meant by
"Figures,"

you must recall that
every syllogism has
three terms.
Let us represent them by
X, Y and Z,
Y being the "middle term,"
the one which does NOT appear in
the conclusion.
Thus the terms
can be arranged in
the following four ways or
"Figures":

	I	II	III	IV
Major premise	YX	XY	YX	XY
Minor premise	ZY	ZY	YZ	YZ
Conclusion	ZX	ZX	ZX	ZX

And so
we are back to 44 cases,
but, fortunately,
they too are not all valid.
Only 24 of these are valid,
and of these
5 are "weak,"
thus leaving only
19 which are
both valid and useful.
To see what is meant by
a "weak" conclusion,
consider the following syllogism:

All material substances gravitate,
All metals are material substances;
Therefore some metals gravitate.

You can see that
you could have concluded that
"All metals gravitate,"
and therefore
to say only that
SOME metals gravitate,
though valid enough,
is obviously
a weaker conclusion
than you would be entitled to.

But this is not all,
for consider
the following quotations from
Jevons, a well-known authority on
Aristotelian Logic:

"In order to facilitate
 the recollection of
 the 19 valid and useful moods
 of the syllogism,
 logicians invented,
 at least six centuries ago,
 a most curious system of
 artificial words,
 combined into mnemonic verses,
 which may be readily
 committed to memory.
 This device, however ingenious,
 is of a barbarous and
 wholly unscientific character;
 but a knowledge of
 its construction and use
 is still expected from
 the student of logic,§

§ Though this was published in 1881,
  it still holds now, in 1960!—
  such is the tenacity
  with which many people cling to
  outmoded ways of thinking!

and the verses are therefore
given and explained below."
And
"Aristotle looked upon
the first figure as
a peculiarly evident and cogent
form of argument—
and he therefore called it the
PERFECT FIGURE.
The fourth figure was
never recognized by him,
and it is often called
the Galenian figure,
because the celebrated Galen
is supposed to have discovered it.
The second and third figures
were known to Aristotle as
the Imperfect Figures,
which it was necessary to reduce
to the first figure by
certain conversions and
transpositions of the premises,
for which directions are to be found
in the artificial words."
The "artificial words"
to which he refers
are given below,
followed by an explanation of
their meaning and use:

Barbara, Celarent, Darii, Ferioque, prioris;
Cesare, Camestres, Festino, Baroco, secundae;
Tertia, *Darapti, Disamis, Datisi, Felapton,*
Bocardo, Ferison, habet;
Quarta insuper addit
Bramantip, Camenes, Dimaris, Fesapo, Fresison.

You will notice that
the italicized words

are NOT real words
in any language,
but have been made up
so that each contains
THREE VOWELS,
representing one of
the remaining 19 Moods (see p. 121).
Thus Barbara represents
the Mood *AAA*, etc.
The words which are
not italicized,
like "prioris," "secundae,"
"Tertia," "Quarta,"
are real Latin words
indicating
which of these moods
are in the first figure,
the second figure,
the third and fourth figures.
Furthermore,
the initial consonant
of each artificial word
indicates to which one
of the four moods of
the first figure
it can be reduced:
thus all those beginning with *B*
can be reduced to Barbara,
those beginning with *C* can be
reduced to Celarent,
etc.
And, furthermore,
each artificial word
contains also
other consonants which show
just how the reduction
is to be made.

For instance,
s indicates that
the proposition denoted by
the preceding vowel
is to be converted "simply,"
which means that
YX is to be re-worded
so that X precedes Y,
thereby converting YX to XY;
thus, instead of saying
"All planets are not self-luminous"
you may say
"No self-luminous bodies are planets."
And m (which comes from
the Latin word "mutare,"
which means "to change")
indicates that
the major and minor premises
are to be interchanged.
You can see that
this does not alter
the meaning of
the syllogism,
but merely helps to change
the figure.

Thus,
to take a standard illustration:
Consider the syllogism:

(1) All stars are self-luminous.
(2) No planets are self-luminous.
(3) Therefore no planets are stars.

This is obviously
in the mood AEE,
and the figure may be
represented by

$$XY$$
$$ZY$$
$$ZX$$

(where X = "stars"

Y = "self-luminous bodies"

Z = "planets")

and is therefore in
the second figure (see p. 121).
Hence it is to be designated by
Camestres (see page 123).
Now this word indicates that
it can be reduced to
Celarent
(because it begins with a C)
by the following procedure:

(1) the *m* tells us to
interchange the
major and minor premises,

(2) the first *s* tells us to
"convert simply"
the proposition represented by
the preceding vowel, e,
namely,
the minor premise,
and

(3) the last *s* tells us to
do the same with
the conclusion.

Thus the syllogism becomes:

(1) No self-luminous bodies are
planets.
(2) All stars are self-luminous.
(3) Therefore no stars are planets.

which is a syllogism in
Celarent.

126

Of course a little consideration
shows clearly that
the meaning of the syllogism
has not been altered,
but the form is now such
that its validity is
easily tested,
since it has now been reduced to
the "Perfect" figure.

For further details
and illustrations
of this process
see page 163.
Also see any standard book on
Traditional Logic.*

And now
where do we go from here?

* For instance,
  "An Introduction to Logic" by
  H. W. B. Joseph
  (Oxford University Press, 1925).

XIV. WHAT THEN?

The syllogisms discussed
in the previous chapter
are known as
"categorical,"
since all three propositions
in each syllogism are
categorical or unconditional ones,
like

$$A \text{ is } B.$$

And these are the only ones
treated in the original
Aristotelian Logic.
Since then, however,
many scholars have added
the "hypothetical" and
"disjunctive"
syllogisms, in which
at least one of the propositions is
"hypothetical" or conditional:
For instance,

(1) Hypothetical:

If A is B, then C is D. ⎫
If C is D, then E is F. ⎬ (Premises)
Therefore if A is B, then E is F. (Conclusion)

(2) Disjunctive:

A is either B or * C. ⎫
But A is B. ⎬ (Premises)

Therefore A is not C. (Conclusion)

* Here "or" means
one of the two alternatives,
but not both.

Later,
after learning
something of
Modern Symbolic Logic,
you will see how
this powerful new tool
boils down both the
categorical and the
hypothetical
syllogisms
to an essence
containing only
a few lines!

Right now, however,
let us look at
some of the
hypothetical syllogisms,
with their picturesque
Latin names which are
still in use;
and let us try to get
a bird's-eye view of
all this
Traditional Logic.

A hypothetical syllogism may be
"pure" or "mixed."
The "pure" ones may be either:

(1) Modus ponens: †

    If A is B, then C is D,
    If C is D, then E is F;
    therefore,
    if A is B, then E is F.

† "Ponens" is
  the Latin word for
  "asserting."

or

(2) Modus tollens: †
    If A is B, then C is D,
    if C is D, E is not F;
    therefore
    if E is F, A is not B.

You may easily make up for yourself
simple illustrations of
these forms of reasoning.

Furthermore, in a
"mixed" hypothetical syllogism
the major premise is
hypothetical, while the
minor premise and the conclusion
are categorical assertions;
and here also we have:

(1) Modus ponens:
    If A is B, C is D,
    but A is B,
    therefore
    C is D.

and

(2) Modus tollens:
    If A is B, C is D,
    but C is not D,
    therefore A is not B.

And, finally in
the disjunctive syllogism,
the major premise is
"disjunctive"
(i.e., it gives two possible

† "Tollens" is Latin for "denying"
  and applies here because of
  the word "not" in this syllogism.

alternatives)
whereas
the minor premise is a
categorical proposition,
which may be
affirmative or negative,
thus:

(1) Modus ponendo tollens: ‡

    A is either B or * C,
    But A is B,
    Therefore A is not C.

or

(2) Modus tollendo ponens: ‡

    A is either B or C,
    But A is not B.
    Therefore A is C.

But perhaps you are beginning
to get one of those
million headaches
referred to by Langer (p. 113),
and are anxious to see
the modern method which

---

‡ "ponendo tollens" means:
  "by asserting" (ponendo)
  something, like A is B,
  we are led to "denying" (tollens)
  something else,
  like A is not C.
  and
  "tollendo ponens" means:
  "by denying" (tollendo)
  something, like A is not B,
  we are led to
  "asserting" (ponens)
  something else,
  like, A is C.
* Here "or" means
  one of the two alternatives
  but not both.

reduces all these words
to a few lines of
clear symbolism.
When you have seen that,
you will see in a nutshell
what syllogistic reasoning
accomplishes,
as well as
having a tool with which
you can go far beyond
the syllogism.

First, however, it will be
worth while to consider that
the study of
traditional logic
exhibited many "fallacies"
which are still being used on
innocent victims
many, many times daily;
and hence
we must still learn to
recognize and destroy them!

But the mere study of
the syllogisms
and the "fallacies"
is not enough.
Modern logic,
as it appears in
Science and Mathematics,
and in the formal study of
Symbolic Logic itself
is essential for
MODERN THINKING!

XV. BEWARE OF THE PITFALLS!

Many logicians have
followed all kinds of
arguments,
legal and otherwise,
and have observed patterns
that have occurred
again and again,
down through the ages,
and are still going on.
So let us look at a few:
The Latin designations for
some of them are:

(1) Argumentum ad hominem
("homo" means "man"),
which refers to
an appeal to purely
personal prejudice
rather than to reason.

(2) Argumentum ad populum
is an appeal to
the prejudices of
a group of people
rather than to reason.

(3) Argumentum ad verecundiam
is an appeal to
respect for some authority
rather than to reason.

(4) Post hoc, ergo propter hoc,
which means
"After this, therefore
 because of this,"

that is,
maintaining that
just because
one thing comes after another
therefore it is caused by it!
For instance,
in some advertising we read,
"She is engaged,
    she uses —— face powder,"
implying that
she is engaged
BECAUSE she uses
this brand of powder.
This type of appeal to desire,
not to reason,
is very commonly used.
And, believe it or not,
it actually influences people
unless they train themselves
to judge a product by
its worth
rather than by
false "arguments."

Another fallacy to be
particularly watched is
the fallacy of References,
in which a writer actually gives
"references" in support of
a statement
to passages which do NOT
really bear it out,
in the trust that
readers will not look up the
references
and discover this." *

* See "An Introduction to Logic"
  by H. W. B. Joseph (p. 574),
  published by Oxford Univ. Press, 1925.

This may seem to you like
a device so childish
that it would never be used by
serious grown-up people,
BUT IT IS,
and we must guard against it.
Recently a candidate for
a very important position
was supposed to have been
discredited in a letter
written by someone who
knew him well.
Subsequently the letter
was shown up as a fraud!
So you see these pitfalls
are not merely of
historical interest
but are being used against us
today.
And of course this applies
with even greater force
to speakers than to writers.
A more modern version of this
is to quote
unfounded "statistics"
which give an air of
Science and Mathematics
but are sometimes
mere frauds
and should therefore be
checked up!

All these things
we poor listeners and readers
have to watch for constantly,
follow up,
check up,
and be generally

awake to
the many types of
verbal frauds that have
come down to us
through the ages,
with new ones
always being added.
But fortunately,
there is a good deal of
repetition of the patterns,
so,
if we are not too gullible
and not too easily intimidated †
and keep our heads clear
and our hearts alive,
we CAN learn
to detect and conquer
these cheap tricks;
but naturally
it takes some training
and effort
on our part.
You can see that
such training and effort are
ESSENTIAL in a DEMOCRACY.
And it can even be FUN
to listen to
speakers on the radio
and elsewhere,
and to read

† Cf. the familiar illustration
  given in standard books on
  Logic:
  "An attorney for the defendant
  in a lawsuit
  is said to have handed
  to the barrister
  his brief marked:
  'No case; abuse the plaintiff's attorney' "
  (see Jevons: "Lessons in Logic").

articles in the papers
and elsewhere,
and look for
what we might call
logical "boners,"
and play the game of
seeing how many of them
we can detect,
either at once,
or after checking
the references and data.‡
You can get yourself
quite a liberal education
by playing this game.
And, if you already have one,
help yourself to another,
to bring you up to date,
for Education must march on
"until death do us part."

‡ This practice will be particularly useful in
election campaigns and other speeches.

XVI. LET SAM BE THE JUDGE!

Sometimes some people say
that they are willing to grant
that the above-mentioned
fallacies
(as well as those in this chapter)
are unreasonable,
but they believe that
it is undesirable to
eliminate them,
because
sometime they may wish
to use them themselves
on somebody else!
Thus,
though they are annoyed
by the filibustering of
the opposing party
(that is, when the "opposition"
merely "hogs the floor,"
talking about all kinds of things
which are not relevant to
the subject under discussion,*
in order to keep others
from talking to the point!)—
still
they hope some day
to use this
"double-edged sword"
against the other party,
and are therefore opposed to
eliminating this practice!
But what does SAM say

* Non sequiturs in a BIG WAY!

about this view?
It is hardly necessary to say
that
this is definitely NOT
in the spirit of SAM!
For in Science and Mathematics
filibustering
is completely ruled out
AND YET
everyone must admit
that SAM's procedures
are ever so much more
SUCCESSFUL
than the
ANTI–SAM–ITIC
practice of
enduring the unreason of
the other fellow
in the hope that
you can get even with him
some day
by the same method!
SAM wants his men
to compete with each other
in being REASONABLE,
and thus
all move forward together,
instead of "opposite" sides
following a policy
of holding both of them back,
since under this scheme
the "winner" is the one
who can make the most noise or
who can "put over"
the "shrewder" scheme.
No wonder that
progress is so slow
and wars increasingly horrible!

While all the time
SAM keeps showing us
a way to
RAPID PROGRESS
and to the
ELIMINATION OF WAR.

And so
let us proceed to
examine some more of
the pitfalls
so that we may all
avoid them together.

Logicians have long
called attention to
the fallacy known as
Equivocation,
in which a word is used
in different senses
within the same syllogism—
"Double-talk"!
This of course
is done on purpose
to confuse,
but, in addition to this,
some people are beginning to
realize more and more
to-day,
that relatively FEW words
have clear, definite meanings,
even though
many people use them
quite confidently and innocently
WITHOUT REALIZING THIS! †

† See "Language in Action" by
 S. I. Hayakawa (Harcourt, Brace & Co., 1941).

Thus even the word
"Democracy"
is now being used
with such different meanings
that it might be wise
to avoid its use entirely
and to think
about specific issues
for the benefit of
all the people
rather than get side-tracked
in fighting over a word
and taking sides
on irrelevant grounds
instead of
striving for the good of
all the people
all over the world,
as SAM does!

And so, also,
with many, many
other words and phrases:
"freedom of speech"
"freedom of enterprise"
etc., etc.,
some of which
are now being
studied anew in
UNESCO,
with the realization
that we must
re-examine their meanings
in a rational manner.
And of course
we cannot leave
this important task
to members of

143

a particular organization alone,
but must,
EACH ONE OF US,
re-examine many
seemingly familiar words
and reconsider their meanings,
if this world is to be
one in which
we can ALL live and be happy
as SAM wants us to be!

And now let us look at
just one more well-known type
of fallacy,
known as "circular reasoning,"
not only because
it is a common type,
but also because
you will see here
how CAREFUL one must be
even in diagnosing it properly,
and how very helpful
a little ordinary algebra
can be!

Thus consider
the following situation:
A man promised his friend
a job on a commission basis
under the following terms:
"Your salary will be
  20% of the net profit,
  but the profit is to be
  considered net AFTER
  your salary
  (as well as all other expenses)
  has been deducted
  from the gross profit."

Now a young man who
had heard a little about
"circular reasoning,"
immediately jumped to the conclusion
that this problem is
"illogical"
because it involves
"circular reasoning,"
and therefore cannot be solved.
Let us examine this a moment.
In the first place
some people think of
"circular reasoning"
(or "Petitio Principii"
or "Begging the Question")
in the following way:
it is arguing that
A depends on B
and when asked
"But how do you know that
B is true?,"
giving the reply,
"Well, it follows from A"—
and thus neither A nor B
has been established.
Applying this idea to
the problem on page 144,
it APPEARS that
since the salary is to
depend upon the net profit,
and the net profit cannot
be determined until
AFTER subtracting this salary
(which is unknown!)
from the gross profit—
hence the problem seems to be
illogical and impossible!
But you will soon see

(1) how vague is this way of
describing circular reasoning,

(2) how easily the above problem
can be solved by algebra,
and

(3) how clear an idea of what
circular reasoning really is
we can get from
Mathematics.‡

Thus, let us first
solve the problem,
to show that it is
a perfectly reasonable one:

> Let $x =$ the gross profit
> Let $y =$ the salary in question
> Let $z =$ all other expenses

Then the net profit
may be expressed by

$$x - y - z.$$

Therefore

$$y = .2(x - y - z)$$

which merely expresses
in algebraic language
the condition that
the salary (y) is equal to
.2 (or 20%) of
the net profit $(x - y - z)$.
Hence,
knowing the gross profit, x,
of the business, say $100,000,
and knowing that
all other expenses (rent, etc.)
amount to say $10,000,
we then have

$$y = .2(100,000 - y - 10,000)$$

‡ See page 184.

or

$$y = .2(90,000 - y)$$

or

$$y = 18,000 - .2y$$

Therefore

$$1.2y = 18,000$$

or

$$12y = 180,000$$

or

$$y = \$15,000$$

as any child knows from
elementary algebra.
In other words,
it is quite simple,
by means of algebra,
to put a problem in
the form of an equation
containing UNKNOWN quantities,
and yet
manipulate them
by simple, reasonable processes,
and soon,
almost mechanically,
arrive at the numerical value
of these quantities which
at first are unknown.§
And it is therefore
unnecessarily confusing to
worry about the above-mentioned

§ See "Take a Number: Mathematics for the Two Billion"
  by Lillian R. Lieber
  with drawings by
  Hugh Gray Lieber
  (Ronald Press Company).

147

FALSE idea of
what "circular reasoning"
really is.
So that,
to a person who,
in the course of his education,
has been confused with
VERBIAGE,
a little algebra will come
like a ray of sunshine!

Later, in Chapter XX,
you will find more
mathematical light
on the very meaning of
"circular reasoning" itself,
for this is a real danger
which we must learn to
guard against.
And so we see that
a LITTLE education is
a dangerous thing,
as we saw above
in the person who
had heard of
"circular reasoning" but
did not really understand it,
and went around
loudly proclaiming that
certain perfectly reasonable
problems
were illogical and unsolvable!
We must beware of
such HALF–EDUCATED DEFEATISM!
And SAM's advice of course is
NOT that we should therefore
go BACK to the good old days of
illiteracy,

but rather
go FORWARD to
MORE knowledge which
will help us
to SOLVE more and more of
our problems.

And now let us take
the old traditional logic
and eliminate from it
all the confusing verbiage,
boil it down to
a FEW LINES of
simple, mathematical symbolism
in order to see clearly
what it is all about
and
what it is good for,
as well as
to go forward
to more and better Logic
so desperately needed in
this MODERN world,
so that
we shall not continue
to be dragged down by
all the antiquated tricks
that have been used for
centuries—
verbiage, noise,
filibustering, fighting,
confusion, et al.

Let SAM take you
by the hand
and be
YOUR LEADER.

Is someone saying
"But can SAM
  eliminate difficulties
  that have been going on for
  centuries?"

To which the answer is:
"Why not give him a chance?
  He has done it many times before.
  Remember penicillin,
  and atomic energy,
  etc., etc.
  These are NEW and
  SAM believes that
  we can use them for our
  GOOD,
  for SAM is NO DEFEATIST!
  He has
  FAITH
  HOPE and
  CHARITY!
  It is in this spirit
  that he is now
  attacking the problem of
  CANCER,
  and will keep at it
  until he conquers it;
  and the problem of the
  ELIMINATION OF WAR
  and will conquer that too.
  But he needs YOUR backing
  in all these problems!
  You must help SAM
  to help YOU."

XVII. CLASSES

On page 111
you saw that
a diagram was helpful
in seeing the
VALIDITY of
an "immediate" conclusion.
And you will now find
that similar diagrams
will be helpful also
in connection with syllogisms.
But first
a little explanation is needed:

(1) It is necessary,
in any discussion,
to state explicitly
what is to be
⋅ the "universe of discourse,"
that is,
to say plainly
what you are going to
talk about.
That is SAM's way,
and avoids getting
off the subject!
Thus if we are going
to talk about
positive, whole numbers only
(1,2,3, . . .)
we must say so,
and then we shall know that
1 ½ is not included in
this "universe of discourse."

ALGEBRA OF CLASSES

$aa = a$ $a + a = a$

(2) We may now "classify"
these numbers
in various ways:
we may form
the class of EVEN numbers,
containing 2,4,6, etc.;
or the class of ODD numbers,
containing 1,3,5, etc.;
or the class of numbers which
are less than 6,
containing only 1,2,3,4,5.
And so on, for other classes.
Of course the largest class
that can be formed here
will contain
ALL the positive integers,
and is called the
"Universe Class" of this
"universe of discourse."

(3) If we designate
by the letter e
the class containing
EVEN numbers only,
then the class containing
all the rest of this
"universe of discourse"
may be designated by e',
and is called
the "complement" of e.
Similarly,
if b is the class containing
only the numbers 1,2,3,4,
then b' is the class containing
all the numbers from 5 up.
The universe class
may be designated by 1.
And the class containing

NONE of the numbers
(the "null" class)
may be designated by o.
You will see that
the "null" class
is as important here
as our familiar o of arithmetic
without which you
could not even write
$1,000,000.

(4) In the following diagram
the rectangle represents
the universe class, 1, and

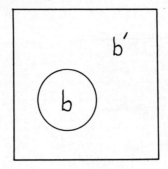

class *b*, with its complement *b'*,
may be represented as shown.

(5) If two classes, *b* and *e*, overlap,
as shown in the next diagram:

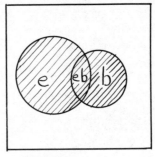

the "sum" * of classes b and e
will be understood to be
the class represented by
the entire shaded portion
as shown.
Thus if class b contains
only the numbers 1,2,3,4,
and class e contains
all even numbers,
then class $b + e$ includes
the numbers 1,2,3,4, and
all the even numbers,
because these are the numbers
which are in b or in e
or in both b and e.

(6) The part common to both
e and b
is called
their "product" * and
is represented by
$e \times b$ or eb.
Thus in our case
eb contains
only the numbers 2 and 4,
because these are the
only numbers which are in
BOTH e and b.

(7) Finally,
if from one or more premises, p,
we can draw
a valid conclusion, q,
it will be represented by

$$p \rightarrow q.$$

* For a justification of this use of
  the words "sum" and "product"
  see Chapter IX.

Now see if you understand
the following cases:

I.

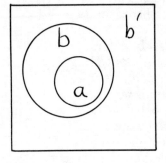

Here $ab' = 0$,
since a is entirely included in b
and obviously has
nothing in common with b',
and therefore their "product" is zero:
$ab' = 0$.

II.

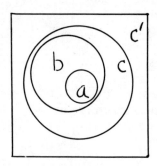

Here $ab' = 0$ again
since a is entirely
included in b.
Similarly $bc' = 0$ because
b is entirely included in c.
Hence you can easily see
the consequence of this,
namely,

      a must be entirely included in **c**

or

$$ac' = 0.$$

In other words:

(1) $ab' = 0$ ⎫
(2) $bc' = 0$ ⎬ (Premises)
(3) Therefore $ac' = 0$ (Conclusion)

Do you recognize
your old friend, Barbara? †
Or did it come on you
too suddenly
and startle you?!

   III.

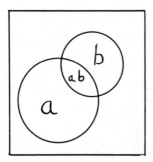

      Here $ab \neq 0$
      since the two classes **overlap**
      and therefore have
      something in common;
      hence their "product"
      is NOT zero:
      $ab \neq 0$
      which means that
      SOME of the members of class *a*
      also belong to class *b*.

† Since the two premises and the conclusion
  are universal affirmative statements
  and hence in the Mood AAA
  (or Barbara).

Suppose you now have

(1) $bc' = 0$
meaning, as before, that
b is entirely within c, } (Premises)
(2) $ab \neq 0$
as shown above,

(3) Therefore
$ac \neq 0$ (Conclusion)
because if you
put class c so that
it includes b
(as demanded by
the major premise)
c will surely contain
SOME of a
(at least the ab part of a),
will it not?
Hence this conclusion is
obviously valid.
Surely you recognize
that this is another of
the syllogisms,
this one being in the mood
   AII ‡
and is in the first figure,§
and therefore in Darii.

Furthermore,
by means of these diagrams,
it is not necessary
to have any

‡ All members of b are in c (A)
  SOME members of a are in b (I)
  Therefore
  SOME members of a are in c (I)
  (See page 117).
§ The figure here is:
   bc ⎫   ⎧ yx ⎫
   ab ⎬ or   ⎨ zy ⎬ p. 121
   ac ⎭   ⎩ zx ⎭

158

negative statements at all,
because
every negative statement
may easily be changed to
a positive one, thus:
Instead of saying that
NONE of a certain type of thing
is in class a,
you may say that
they are ALL in class a',
as shown in the following diagram:

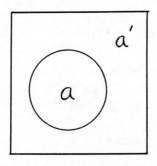

Thus E may always be changed to A (see page 117).
And instead of saying
"SOME members of b are NOT in c,"
you may obviously say:
"SOME members of b ARE in c',"
as shown in the diagram below:

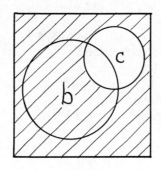

Here the shaded portion
represents c',
which obviously has
in common with b
the very part that is
NOT common to b and c.
Thus
O may be replaced by I (see p. 117),
eliminating
Celarent and Ferio (p. 123)
entirely,
leaving us with
Barbara and Darii only,
which may be briefly written,
as explained above:

(1) $ab' = o$ and $bc' = o \longrightarrow ac' = o$
$\qquad\qquad$ (Barbara)
(2) $bc' = o$ and $ab \neq o \longrightarrow ac \neq o$
$\qquad\qquad$ (Darii)

where the symbol $\longrightarrow$
merely means
"validly leads to,"
as in (7) on p. 155.

And so you can see that
all the VALID syllogisms
can be boiled down to
these two lines (1) and (2) above!
For
it is not even necessary
to perform any "conversions"
since ab is the same as ba
(both expressions representing
the common part of
the same two classes, a and b),
and, of course,
reversing the order of

the two premises is unnecessary,
since this does not
change the meaning
in any way.

There is only one further point
that must be made
in order to hand you
the entire subject of
categorical syllogisms
in that promised nutshell.
And that is
that since traditional logic
did not allow for
the "null" class,
whereas the modern study of classes
does include this class * (see p. 154)
one more statement must be made
to rule out the null class
from the new class notation
if we wish to see
exactly how to express
Aristotelian Logic
in the modern notation.
Hence,

(3) $a \neq 0$ and $ab' = 0$ and $bc' = 0 \longrightarrow ac \neq 0$.

Here, as usual,
$ab' = 0$ means that
a is entirely within b,
and similarly
$bc' = 0$ means that

* For otherwise we could not
  so conveniently write $ab = 0$,
  which says that
  the product of classes a and b
  is equal to the "null" class,
  and which merely means that
  a and b have no members in common.

b is entirely within *c*;
but, in addition,
in order to draw
the conclusion *ac* $\neq$ o,
namely that
a and *c* actually have
SOMETHING in common
(as in Barbara)
it is necessary to
include the premise *a* $\neq$ o,
namely,
that class *a* itself
is not empty.

THUS THE ENTIRE SUBJECT OF
CATEGORICAL SYLLOGISMS
IS SUMMED UP IN:

(1) $ab' = $ o and $bc' = $ o $\longrightarrow ac' = $ o
(2) $bc' = $ o and $ab \neq $ o $\longrightarrow ac \neq $ o
(3) $a \neq $ o and $ab' = $ o and $bc' = $ o $\longrightarrow ac \neq $ o.

As Langer says: ¶
"For a true Aristotelian,
 this exhausts the abstract system
 of logic.
 Later generations of scholars,
 however,
 have added to the
 Aristotelian structure
 the two syllogisms of
 compound propositions,
 known respectively as
 the hypothetical and the disjunctive."
(discussed above on page 128 ff).
These will be
quite easily streamlined
in Chapter XXIII.

¶ See page 113.

But first you may wish to see
in a specific illustration
how neatly this
new symbolism works,
by comparison with
the old way.

Take the following syllogism:
(1) All P is M
(2) Some S is not M
(3) Therefore some S is not P.
The problem is to find out
whether the conclusion is valid.

Let us do it the old way first:

You can see that
this syllogism is in the mood AOO,
and is therefore in Baroco,
is it not?
Now the c in Baroco
(which stands for the Latin
"conversio syllogismi")
"indicates that we must employ **
the process of
Indirect Reduction.—
Indirect Reduction, or
Reductio per impossibile,
consists in showing,
by a syllogism in the
first figure,
against which no objection can
be taken,
that the falsity of the conclusion

** From "An Introduction to Logic" by
H. W. B. Joseph (pp. 291 ff).
By permission of Oxford University Press, New York.

163

in the original syllogism
is inconsistent with
the truth of its premisses.
This is done as follows:
Baroco is of the form

All P is M	All negroes have curly hair.
Some S is not M	Some natives of Africa have not curly hair.
∴ Some S is not P.	∴ Some natives of Africa are not negroes.

Now if this conclusion is false,
its contradictory will be true,
i.e., that
All natives of Africa are negroes.
We can then combine this with our
original major premise to form a
syllogism in Barbara, thus:

All P is M	All negroes have curly hair.
All S is P	All natives of Africa are negroes.
∴ All S is M	∴ All natives of Africa have curly hair.

But the conclusion thus obtained
contradicts the original
minor premiss;
hence if the original premisses
are true,
the conclusion we drew from them
cannot be false,
and our original syllogism
is therefore valid."

Let us now examine the problem
the new way,
using the following diagram:

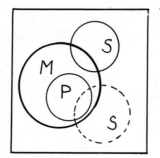

Here:

(1) $PM' = o$ (Major premise)
(2) $SM' \neq o$ (Minor premise)
(3) $\therefore SP' \neq o$ (Conclusion)

Hence the conclusion is valid.

Now, candidly,
don't you like the new way better?!

†† Note that
 although S may be placed
 in various ways,
 still, in any case,
 SOME S is outside of M
 (in accordance with the minor premise)
 and therefore surely outside of P,
 which is briefly expressed by
 $SP' \neq o$

XVIII. SOME FUN

The diagrams in
the previous chapters
were supposed to have been
first used by
the celebrated mathematician
Euler,*
in his letters to a princess
(sometime during the
eighteenth century).
And more extensive use of them
was made by
Venn †
toward the end of the
nineteenth century,
so that they are now called
Venn diagrams.‡

As you have already seen,
they are very simple to use;
and, since a good, easy
familiarity with them
will make the rest of this book
so intelligible to you,
it would be advisable
for you to express
each side of

* See "Lessons in Logic"
  by W. S. Jevons (Macmillan, 1881).
† "Symbolic Logic"
  by John Venn (London, 1894).
‡ "A Survey of Modern Algebra"
  by Garrett Birkhoff and
  Saunders MacLane
  (Macmillan, 1941).

each of the following equations
in the form of a
Venn diagram
and thus actually see that
both sides of each equation
really represent the
SAME class,
and that is why
it is legitimate to write
an = sign between them.

This will be
at least as much fun as
crossword puzzles or
jigsaw puzzles,—
and so practical besides,
since it will lead you
by an easy path
to a knowledge of
Modern Logic!

And so,
have a little fun
with yourself.

If you have studied
ordinary algebra,
you may think that
you can test these equations by
substituting numbers
in place of the letters,
but this is NOT so,
at least NOT for ALL the
equations.
You must test them by
the use of Venn diagrams!

Now try your skill:

(1) $a + a = a$
(2) $a \times a = a$
(3) $a + b = b + a$
(4) $a \times b = b \times a$
(5) $(a + b) + c = a + (b + c)$
(6) $(a \times b) \times c = a \times (b \times c)$
(7) $a + (b \times c) = (a + b) \times (a + c)$
(8) $a \times (b + c) = (a \times b) + (a \times c)$
(9) $a + ab = a$
(10) $a \times (a + b) = a$
(11) $a \times 1 = a$
(12) $a + 1 = 1$
(13) $a + 0 = a$
(14) $a \times 0 = 0$
(15) $a + a' = 1$
(16) $a \times a' = 0$
(17) If $a = b'$, then $b = a'$
(18) $a = (a')'$
(19) $ab + ab' = a$
(20) $(a + b) \times (a + b') = a$
(21) $(a + b)' = a' \times b'$
(22) $(a \times b)' = a' + b'$

And now that you have had
some fun with
Venn's diagrams,
let us see
what SAM did with them.
That boy not only
has fun with everything,
but
his games turn out to be
so practical
that they will lead us to
SURVIVAL and HAPPINESS
if we play along with him.

The main point is
NOT TO LISTEN TO
THE "EVIL ONE"
who tells people to
fight each other
and destroy this
lovely world!

Who shall be our
LEADER,
SAM or the EVIL ONE?
THAT is the question!
And the answer is
so easy:

If we want LIFE
then the ONLY LEADER is SAM.
And anyone who
REALLY believes that
the EVIL ONE is stronger
and that
destruction of the human race
is inevitable,
would do well for himself if
he would just
lie down and die peacefully
right now,
instead of waiting for
the horrible death and destruction
that he thinks are so inevitable.
Incidentally,
the rest of us,
who are NOT such defeatists,
could say
"Good riddance"
and get to work to
make this the fine world that
SAM has in mind for us.

Do you not think that
the very fact
that these defeatists
do NOT commit suicide
means that
deep down in their hearts
they too think there is some
HOPE,
and, to that extent at least,
there may be a chance
to convert even them
to SAM's philosophy!
Perhaps it is this very
confusion in
their own minds
which makes them
"throw fits"
like Pavlov's
poor confused dogs (see p. 172).
Or do they believe
that they alone
can be spared,
contrary to the opinion
of SAM's men, who
know the modern facts
better than anyone else!
(See Part I of this book.)

XIX. POSTULATIONAL THINKING

To see how
SAM further improved and enriched
Logic,
you must become familiar with
"postulational thinking,"
which you will love
for its clarity and power!

As you probably know,
before Euclid (300 B.C.)
quite a little geometry
was known,
but it was just
a lot of isolated bits of
information,
not connected until
Euclid put it into a
"system."
This he did by
first listing
what he considered to be
"self-evident truths,"
and then deriving from these,
by logic,
the "consequences"
or "inferences"
or "conclusions"
or "theorems."
The advantage of such a system
is obvious,
for,
in the first place,
a system shows

the interrelationships of
various bits of knowledge
and makes it easier
to understand and remember them.
But, more than this,
it enables us to make sure
that
at least in the basic ideas
(of which there are not many)
there are no contradictions—
for contradictions are
abhorrent to SAM.

You see he knows about
those experiments by
Pavlov,*
on the "conditioned reflexes" in dogs,
in which a dog was "conditioned"
to react pleasantly at
the sight of a circle,
and unpleasantly at
the sight of an ellipse,
and then
when the dog was shown
an ellipse that was
so nearly like a circle that
he could not tell
which it was,
the poor dog had
a violent fit!
Living creatures cannot bear
to be in a state in which
they are pulled
in opposite directions

* See "Conditioned Reflexes"
  by I. P. Pavlov
  (Oxford Univ. Press, 1928).

physically or mentally.
And SAM knows it!

And so
if we do not even know
a person's BASIC ideas
in a certain discussion
(or our own BASIC ideas
for that matter),
we cannot tell whether
they are contradictory or not
and therefore whether
his conclusions
are drawn validly or not.
He may be just
going around in "circles,"
never really proving anything,
and all we can do is
just to listen helplessly,
trying to make
a bit of sense here and there,
but not really knowing
what he is driving at.
You can see that
this kind of discussion
is fertile ground for
confusion and strife.
And, if our "friend" happens
to use a "fighting word,"
we suddenly feel
"That does it!"
and the fight is on.
Have you not heard
many discussions
of this kind?
But SAM does not care for it!
(DO YOU?)
That is why he insists that

his Mathematicians,
Logicians and Scientists,
EXPLICITLY state their
BASIC ideas,
and WRITE them down,
for otherwise
we forget them and
start contradicting ourselves
and creating confusion.
Many a worthless "argument"
could be eliminated by
this device alone.

Furthermore,
in the course of time,
the Mathematicians realized
that the BASIC ideas
were not really
"self-evident truths,"—
for in 1826,
Lobachevsky
(as well as Gauss and Bolyai,
quite independently of him)
made a new "system" of
geometry,
in which
all but one of
Euclid's basic ideas
were retained,
but that ONE was changed;
and he found that
he could,
by means of logic,
derive the consequences
of this new basic set of ideas,
which turned out to be
quite different from Euclid's,
resulting in

a "Non-Euclidean Geometry" †
now known to be
extremely important and useful.

Thus it was realized that
a set of BASIC ideas
is merely a collection of
ASSUMPTIONS or
POSTULATES,
and one can reason validly
from any set!
Thus you can say:
"If I were a king,
  then . . ."
Here your BASIC idea is
your being a king
(which may not be true at all),
and from this
certain consequences would follow.
And so
Mathematicians realized that
all that they were really doing
was
to study how to find out
what ARE the consequences
that follow from
ANY given set of POSTULATES.
And, by this time,
they have examined
many different postulate sets,
and created many different
"systems,"
some of which have
already found
practical applications,
and others will undoubtedly

† See the book referred to on p. 108.

find more.
But
the Mathematician is
not really concerned with
these applications
(that is the job of
the Scientists or
of anyone whose business it is
to apply the Mathematics
to something)—
the Mathematician's business is
merely
to DRAW CONCLUSIONS VALIDLY;
that is his specialty,
and that is why
he has built up,
in modern times,
so many systems which
are waiting for us
to use and apply them
to various needs.

You might say,
"How do you know that
anyone will ever find
any uses for them?
Are they not perhaps
just games
that the Mathematicians
are playing with themselves?"
SAM's answer is that
since, in the past,
many of these systems
HAVE found applications,
the probability is very high
that they will do it again.
Note that
SAM does not arrogantly say

"Yes, they surely will!"
He always talks in terms of
PROBABILITY—
merely that some things are
more probable than others.
He is cautious and modest,
and altogether
the gentleman,
don't you think?
(But please do not mistake him
for a Goat in a
"stuffed shirt";
on the contrary,
he is natural and at ease,
and loves music and dancing,—
remember?)

Furthermore,
SAM points out that,
even if some of the systems
do not find applications,
still they are very practical
because they show us
HOW TO THINK STRAIGHT,
and what can be
more practical than that?
"But," you may say,
"surely the Scientists also
have to think straight,
and how can they use
Postulational Thinking
when postulates are
mere assumptions?!
Surely they have to
start with
TRUE basic ideas,
or they would not work!"

To which SAM replies that
it would be wonderful
if we could know
the TRUE basic ideas,
but since we cannot,
the next best thing is
to make assumptions
that seem to fit the observations
in the best and simplest manner,
and then
derive the consequences
(by mathematical methods)
and TEST them!
Thus it takes a GENIUS
    (like Einstein or Newton)
    propose assumptions
    which are adequate to
    the data of the times—
    and of course
the more observations
the assumptions have to satisfy,
the harder it is
to find adequate ones,
so that a MODERN Scientist
has to be
super-sophisticated
and wise!
Hats off, please!

And so
the pattern for thinking is:

(1) Start with
     ASSUMPTIONS
     which seem adequate
     for your purpose.

(2) State them EXPLICITLY
    (Write them out!
    and have VERY FEW of them!)

(3) Make sure they
    DO NOT CONTRADICT
    each other! ‡

(4) Derive the consequences
    which logically follow
    from these.

(5) TEST the consequences.

Try this on some problem,
and do it
conscientiously and calmly.
Do not expect too much
at first.
It takes time
to do a good job.
Studying with SAM
will certainly help!
If we would start this
in early childhood,
on simple problems,
we would become
quite good at it,
for SAM's achievements
are certainly
the "success story"
of all time!

But where does
LOGIC come in?

‡ For a discussion of
  how this can sometimes be done
  see J. W. Young's
  "Fundamental Concepts of Algebra and Geometry"
  (Macmillan, 1920).

Ah, that is
the essence of (4) above,
which says
"Derive the consequences."
LOGIC shows us
HOW to
"derive the consequences"
BEFORE
they really happen to us!
It shows us
HOW to FORETELL
WHAT the consequences will be!
If they are good,
let us go on,
by all means.
But,
if they are bad,
let us avert them
and PREVENT trouble.
Thus SAM's MEN and WOMEN
now FORESEE
the CONSEQUENCES of
using atomic energy
for the making of bombs
instead of for
the BENEFIT of mankind! §
Read again
Einstein's historic
TELEGRAM TO THE PEOPLE
(meaning YOU)
on page 29—
and BE SURE to
DO SOMETHING
about it!!!!

§ We must follow the advice of
   the Atomic Scientists in this matter
   (Subscribe to their Bulletin,
   mentioned on p. 50).

You are not just reading a book—
This is URGENT!

DO IT NOW,
OBEY THAT IMPULSE!
before you continue reading
this book.

XX. BOOLEAN ALGEBRA

Are you learning how
To follow SAM's advice?

This is your best
INSURANCE
against
CATASTROPHE.

If you realize that
part of your
daily business
from now on
is to
convince everyone you know
that
WAR MUST BE STOPPED,
that
ONE WORLD
has now become
IMPERATIVE,
that
we MUST join up with
SAM,
our friend and guide,—
then
you may wish to read more about
LOGIC,
for you will need it

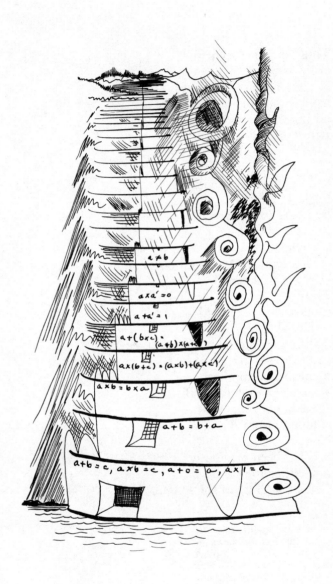

$a \neq b$

$a \times a' = 0$

$a + a' = 1$

$a + (b \times c) =$
$(a+b) \times (a+c)$

$a \times (b+c) = (a \times b) + (a \times c)$

$a \times b = b \times a$

$a + b = b + a$

$a+b = c,\ a \times b = c,\ a + 0 = a,\ a \times 1 = a$

if you are here
"to tell the tale."

Thus you have seen that
every "system,"
like Euclidean Geometry,
has a certain definite set of
postulates.*
Before telling you
what is meant by
"Boolean Algebra"
and its connection with
Logic,
let us see first how
the very idea of
a postulate set
throws light on the question of
"circular reasoning" (see p. 146).
Thus
suppose you are asked
to PROVE
a certain geometric proposition, **A,**
and suppose you prove it
by means of another
geometric proposition, *B*
(that is, you show that
A follows from *B*).
Now,
if *B* has been previously
established from the
POSTULATES of the system,

---

* As a matter of fact
  there are various such sets,
  but they can be shown to be
  "equivalent" to each other
  so long as we stay
  within the boundaries of
  one system, say,
  "Euclidean Geometry."

then your proof of A
is VALID.
But, if B has NOT been
so derived,
and if you then proceed
to prove B by means of A,
which has also NOT been
derived from the
POSTULATES,
then you are using
"circular reasoning,"
making A depend upon B
and B upon A,
without having established
the validity of either one,
because
the VALIDITY of any proposition
means that
it follows from the
POSTULATES themselves
(either directly or
via some other propositions which
have themselves been shown to be
VALID,
in the sense described above).

And so,
whereas the Venn diagrams
are helpful,
SAM is not satisfied UNTIL
we clearly exhibit
the set of
POSTULATES
of the system which we are
considering here,
so that we may be sure
that we are not just
going around in "circles."

This will be done in
the present chapter,
and you will find that
the system in question here
is known as
"Boolean Algebra." †
You will find also that
the equations on page 168
all belong to this "algebra,"
which is UNLIKE
ordinary algebra in many respects,
although there are points of
likeness, too.

You can of course
compare and contrast
these two algebras
by substituting
NUMBERS for the letters
in the above-mentioned equations,
to see which of these equations
hold good in
ordinary algebra,
whereas
the letters represent
CLASSES (NOT NUMBERS)‡
in Boolean Algebra.

And so,
let us examine a set of

† First suggested by
  George Boole:
  "An Investigation of the
   Laws of Thought"
  (Macmillan, 1854).
‡ CLASSES are not the ONLY
  possible interpretation of
  the letters in
  Boolean Algebra,
  as you will see in
  Chapters XXII and XXIV.

POSTULATES for Boolean Algebra,
or the "Algebra of Classes":

Here, as explained in
Chapter XVII,
a, b, c, a', etc. represent
classes,
1 represents the
universe class,
o represents the null class,
+ and × having the meanings
given in that chapter.

Following are the Postulates:

(1) If a and b are any two classes,
then their sum, $a + b$,
is a certain definite class
of the system.

(2) Similarly for the product:
$a \times b$ is a
certain definite class
of the system.

(3) $a + o = a$,
which says that
if the null class is added
to any class,
it leaves that class
unchanged.

(4) $a \times 1 = a$,
i.e., the part which is common
to any class, a, and
the universe class, 1,
is the class, a, itself.

(5) $a + b = b + a$,
i.e., when adding two classes,
it is immaterial which one

is taken first.
In other words,
Addition here is Commutative
(just as in
ordinary algebra).

(6) Similarly for Multiplication:
$a \times b = b \times a$,
i.e., Multiplication is also
Commutative
(as it is also in
ordinary algebra).

(7) Similarly
$a \times (b + c) = (a \times b) + (a \times c)$,
which says that
Multiplication is
distributive over Addition
(which also holds in ordinary
arithmetic and algebra).

(8) $a + (b \times c) = (a + b) \times (a + c)$,
which says that
Addition is "distributive" over
Multiplication
(which does NOT hold in
ordinary arithmetic and
algebra—
try it and see).

(9) $a + a' = 1$,
that is, any class when
added to its own complement
gives the universe class
(see Chapter XVII).

(10) $a \times a' = 0$,
which says that
any class has nothing in common with
its own complement.

(11) There are
AT LEAST two different classes
in the system,
though of course
there may be more.

You can easily see that
all these postulates
EXCEPT (8), (9) and (10)
hold also for numbers in
ordinary algebra,
whereas of course
they ALL hold for CLASSES in
Boolean Algebra.

Among the "exercises" on p. 168
you will find some of these
POSTULATES,
namely,
you can find among those exercises
the following postulates:
(3), (4), (5), (6), (7), (8), (9),
and (10).

And all the remaining exercises
would have to be
PROVED,
that is,
one would have to show that
each of them can be
derived from the postulates.

It is not necessary to do that here,
since, if you are interested,
you can find such proofs
in books on

189

Symbolic Logic.*
But,
to get the spirit of "proof,"
it will interest you
to see a few of these,
especially, in particular,
the proofs of
Barbara and Darii.

And it might be helpful
to arrange these proofs
as we have all been
brought up to do in school
in studying Euclidean Geometry—
namely,
writing the statements and
the reasons for them
clearly,
next to each other,
remembering of course that
the only legitimate "reasons"
are the basic rules (postulates)
themselves
(or "theorems" which have
previously been so proved).

Thus let us prove first that

$$a \times o = o.$$

Since this is NOT among
the eleven postulates,
it must be PROVED,
no matter how reasonable
it may seem to your

* A very readable book is
"Introduction to Symbolic Logic"
by S. K. Langer
(Houghton Mifflin, 1937).

more easily than
you can drive around,
but nevertheless,
if you learn to drive,
you will then have
a means of
"going places"
that you could never have if
you stuck to walking.
And so, here,
you are learning to use
Boolean Algebra,
basing all your arguments
on its postulates
and not on
any other consideration,
such as diagrams, etc.,
though whenever such
diagrams help you,
you may use them to guide you,
though they are NOT acceptable
in a formal proof—
since strict reliance on
the postulates
has been found to be
the safest method.
And, indeed,
in more difficult problems,
you will find that
these diagrams
are no longer so helpful,
so the wise thing is
to practice
and get skill
in formal proofs.

And now let us PROVE
Barbara and Darii.

"intuition."
Note that
in Chapter XVII,
all conclusions were drawn
"intuitively,"
and that was
acceptable as a tentative start,
but SAM demands
that results
must be derived by
meticulously showing
that they follow from the
BASIC POSTULATES,
and that nothing else
"sneaks in,"
either through carelessness
or by deliberate intent!

That is how
HONEST and CAREFUL
SAM is!

I. And so let us

PROVE $a \times o = o$ (or $a \cdot o = o$)

Proof

Statements		Reasons	
(1)	$(a \cdot o) = (a \cdot o) + o$	Postulate	(3)
(2)	$= o + (a \cdot o)$	Postulate	(5)
(3)	$= (a \cdot a') + (a \cdot o)$	Postulate	(10)
(4)	$= a(a' + o)$	Postulate	(7)
(5)	$= a \cdot a'$	Postulate	(3)
(6)	$= o$	Postulate	(10)

And so it has been
PROVED
that $a \cdot o = o$

II. Here is another one:

To prove $ab' = 0 \longrightarrow a = ab$

That is:

If we have given that $ab' = 0$
we can PROVE from it that
$a = ab$:

Proof

Statements		Reasons
(1)	$ab + 0 = ab$	Postulate (3)
(2)	$ab' = 0$	Given
(3)	$\therefore \quad ab + ab' = ab$	Since $ab' = 0$
(4)	$\therefore \quad a(b + b') = ab$	Postulate (7)
(5)	$\therefore \quad a(1) = ab$	Postulate (9)
(6)	$\therefore \quad a = ab$	Postulate (4)

If this result seems
"strange,"
please remember that
a and b are NOT numbers,
but CLASSES,
and what you have just proved
is shown in
the following diagram:

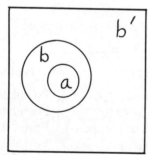

Here the rectangle is
the boundary within which
are all the classes of the set;
among them are a and b,
b' being the complement of b

(that is, the class containing
all the classes not in b);
hence $ab' = 0$ merely
expresses the fact that
a and b' have no classes in common
(and hence a is entirely within b).
And it has been proved
that the consequence of this is
that $a = ab$,
which simply means that
the part common to a and b
(represented, as usual, by ab)
is the class a itself,
a result which is
easily verified from
the diagram on p. 192.

Perhaps you are thinking that
you follow the argument better
from the diagram
than from the formal proof
written out on page 192.
But of course you must realize that:

(1) "intuitional" ideas
require "checking";
the "feeling" that
we are right
may be misleading!

(2) whenever we are trying
to learn to use
any new machine,
we are a little unhappy about it
at first.
Thus when learning
to drive a car
you can no doubt
walk around the block

XXI. BARBARA AND DARII

As you already know,
in a formal proof of
any proposition
(like Barbara or Darii),
each statement made
must be derived
either
directly from the postulates
or
via other propositions which
have already been
so derived.
Now,
in the proof of Barbara,
we shall need (6) on page 168,
namely,
$(ab)c = a(bc)$,
which
has not yet been proved here.
Now since the proof of (6)
is rather long,
and since you can easily
look it up,*
let us now proceed with
the proof of Barbara,
which may be stated
as follows
(see p. 160):

* See Appendix B in
  "Introduction to Symbolic Logic"
  by S. K. Langer,
  previously mentioned.

Given: $ab' = 0$ and $bc' = 0$
To prove: $ac' = 0$

Proof

Statements	Reasons
(1) $ab' = 0$	Given
(2) $\therefore a = ab$	Proved on p. 192
Similarly, from $bc' = 0$ (which is also given) we can get $b = bc$	
(3) $\therefore$ (2) becomes $a = a(bc)$	By substitution
(4) But $a(bc) = (ab)c$	See †
(5) $\therefore$ (3) becomes $a = (ab)c$	By substitution
(6) But $ab = a$	See (2)
(7) $\therefore$ (5) becomes $a = ac$	By substitution
(8) $\therefore ac' = acc'$	Since a is the same as ac from (7)
(9) But $cc' = 0$	Postulate (10)
(10) $\therefore a(cc') = 0$	Proved on p. 191
(11) $\therefore (ac)c' = 0$	See step (4)
(12) $\therefore ac' = 0$	Substituting in (11) a for ac from (7).

And so
Barbara has been
rigorously justified!

And now let us do as much
for Darii:

† See footnote, p. 195.

Darii may be stated thus
(see page 160):

Given: $bc' = 0$ and $ab \neq 0$
To prove: $ac \neq 0$

Proof

Statements	Reasons
(1) $ab \neq 0$	Given
(2) $\therefore$ $a \neq 0$ and $b \neq 0$	For, if either of these were equal to zero, ab would have to equal zero (see p. 191)
(3) $bc' = 0$	Given
(4) $\therefore$ $b = bc$	Proved on p. 192
(5) $\therefore$ replacing b by bc in (1), it becomes $a(bc) \neq 0$	By substitution
(6) or $a(cb) \neq 0$	Postulate (6)
(7) $\therefore$ $(ac)b \neq 0$	See p. 195
(8) $\therefore$ $ac \neq 0$	See step (2) above.

And so
both Barbara and Darii
are now
firmly established
in fine modern style!

Let us now briefly
take stock of
what has been accomplished
and where we go from here:

I. Aristotelian Logic
has been
BOILED DOWN
and put on a
FIRM, MODERN BASIS.‡

II. The scope of the
Algebra of Classes,
simple as it is,
is much more inclusive than
the categorical syllogism,
which is summed up in
ONLY THREE THEOREMS
of this Algebra!—
See the proofs of
Barbara and Darii (pp. 196 and 197)
and (3) on page 162.

III. The model for
clear, modern thinking
has turned out to have
the same "pattern" as
a GAME,
namely,

(1) We must first
state clearly
what the "equipment" is to be—
that is,
the things or "elements"
with which we shall "play"
(whether "numbers" or "classes,"
or what have you).

‡ So far this has been done here
for categorical syllogisms only.
For the hypothetical and
disjunctive ones
see Chapter XXIII.

(2) We must then
state clearly
what we are supposed
"to do" with the equipment,
that is,
what are the "operations"
which we are to perform
upon the elements.

(3) Finally, we must
state clearly
what are the "rules" or
"postulates"
that govern the game.

Now isn't that simple?

And besides,
SAM's games
are not only
more fun than
other games
(to which you will
surely agree,
if you play some of them),
but also turn out to be
so PRACTICAL besides,
as you will soon see in
some Applications.

XXII. ANSWER "YES" OR "NO"

Before going into these
Applications,
let us take one more look at
Boolean Algebra
and compare it with
ordinary Algebra.
In the latter, as you know,
we may write

$$2^3 = 2 \times 2 \times 2 = 8$$

where the little number $(^3)$,
(called the "exponent")
shows how many times
the large number (2)
(called the "base")
is to be used as a factor;
similarly

$$5^2 = 5 \times 5 = 25$$

etc.
And therefore, in general,

$$x^n \neq x$$

But, in the
Algebra of Classes
(Boolean Algebra)

$$x^2 = x \cdot x = x$$

since here the "product" of
two classes
is their common part,
and obviously the part
common to x and x
is x itself.

Hence, also,

$$x^3 = x \cdot x^2 = x \cdot x = x$$

and, in general,

$$x^n = x$$

so that here,
no matter how many x's
are multiplied together,
the answer is always x,
thus making
exponents unnecessary
in this Algebra!

The children would like
this Algebra,
don't you think?

Furthermore,
in ordinary Algebra

$$x + x + x = 3x \text{ and}$$
$$x + x + x + x + x = 5x$$

etc.,
the number in front of the x
(like the 3 or 5),
called the "coefficient" of x,
shows how many x's
were added together.
But, in the Algebra of Classes,

$$x + x = x$$

(see the definition of
"addition" of classes on p. 155),
and therefore

$$x + (x + x) = x + x = x$$

Thus, no matter how many x's

are added together,
the answer is always x,
so that
coefficients are also unnecessary!

Do we hear another cheer
from the children?
Do they like this new Algebra?
No doubt about it!

However,
they must of course
NOT get the idea that
they can now throw away
ordinary Algebra,
the Algebra of numbers which
we all study in school,
since they will still need it
for doing accounts and
figuring income taxes and
solving all the ordinary
algebraic problems.
But,
for the study of LOGIC,
which is just as practical
for daily life,
it is the NEW, EASY
Boolean Algebra
that we need!
You will soon see that
one of the many Applications
of this Algebra
is in the study of
electrical circuits in
a telephone company—
now what can be more
"practical"
than that?

But first
let us take
the eleven postulates of
Boolean Algebra (page 187 ff.)
and add one more,

(12) $a = 1$ or $a = 0$,

thus limiting the Algebra to
ONLY TWO CLASSES,
the universe class (1)
and the null class (0),
and of course
retaining all the other
eleven postulates.
This special type of
Boolean Algebra
is, as you see,
even simpler than
the one discussed before.
Perhaps you may think that
this is too simple
to be of any use.
But, as a matter of fact,
this super-simple Algebra,
which has only
TWO elements in it,
is the very one used in
the study of electrical circuits,
as well as in
other applications,
as you will see!

Not only that—
it is also this
super-simple Algebra
which is applicable to
what is called
"The Algebra of Propositions,"

which exhibits clearly
what is the very nature of
the kind of thinking
that has been employed here
so far,
including what are known as
"the Laws of Thought"
in Traditional Logic,
namely:

(1) the Law of Contradiction
(2) the Law of
    "Excluded Middle"
(3) the Law of Identity.

Let us therefore
take a look at
"the Algebra of Propositions":

(1) The "elements" in
    this "universe of discourse"
    are "propositions"
    (designated by p, q, r, etc.),
    where a "proposition" is
    a categorical statement.
    Also,
    p' is the negative of p;
    thus,
    if p is the proposition
    "All numbers are even,"
    then p' is the proposition
    "Not all numbers are even."
    Further,
    1 represents "truth" and
    0 represents "falsity."
    And $(p')'$ is the same as p.

(2) The "operations" are
    disjunction (represented by v) and

conjunction (represented by $\cdot$).
$p \vee q$ is to be read
"p or q or both."
$p \cdot q$ is to be read
"p and q."

(3) The postulates are
the following twelve
and will be presently discussed:

1. $p \vee q = r$
2. $p \cdot q = r$
3. $p \vee o = p$
4. $p \cdot 1 = p$
5. $p \vee q = q \vee p$
6. $p \cdot q = q \cdot p$
7. $p \cdot (q \vee r) = (p \cdot q) \vee (p \cdot r)$
8. $p \vee (q \cdot r) = (p \vee q) \cdot (p \vee r)$
9. $p \vee p' = 1$
10. $p \cdot p' = o$
11. $p \neq q$
12. $(p = 1) \vee (p = o)$

You cannot help noticing that
these twelve postulates
are very reminiscent of
the twelve postulates for
the Algebra of Classes,
eleven of which are
given on pages 187–189
and
postulate (12) on page 204.
Indeed,
either of these sets of
postulates
may be "translated"
into the other

with the aid of
the following "dictionary":

Language of Classes	Language of Propositions
a, b, c, · · ·	p, q, r, · · ·
+	v
×	·
o	o
1	1
a'	p'

Thus,
the statement that
class a is entirely included
in class b,
as shown in the diagram:

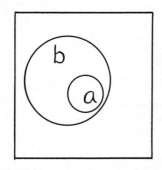

can be "translated" into
the Language of Propositions
by saying:
The proposition (p) that
"Something is a member of class a"
would "imply" *
the proposition (q) that
"It is also a member of class b."

* "Implication" will be discussed further
in Chapter XXIII.

Furthermore.
the class $a + b$
is represented by
the shaded portion in the diagram:

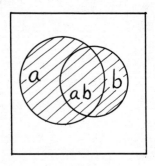

and refers to members which are
either in a or in b or in both,
and therefore you can
express this,
in the Language of Propositions,
by

$$p \vee q$$

(see p. 206 for the description of
the symbol $\vee$).

Similarly
the class "product" ab
refers to the class containing
members of BOTH a and b
as shown in the diagram above,
and therefore,
when translated into the
Language of Propositions,
becomes

$$p \cdot q$$

(see page 206).

Remember that
the addition of Postulate (12)
(page 204)
limited the system to
TWO classes ONLY,
so that class *a* can have
only two possible "values,"
either the universe class, 1, or
the null class, 0.

Similarly
in this Algebra of Propositions,
Postulate (12) on page 206
says that
p can have
only two possible "values,"
either "truth," 1,
or "falsity," 0.
This means, of course,
that any propositions
which are
"doubtful" or "ambiguous"
or have to be qualified in any way
are ruled out in
this "universe of discourse."

Furthermore,
Postulate (10) (page 206):

$$p \cdot p' = 0$$

says that
a proposition, *p*,
and its negative, *p'*
cannot BOTH be true,
which is really
the Law of Contradiction
mentioned on page 205.

And Postulate (9):

$$p \vee p' = 1$$

says that
either p or p' †
MUST be true,
which is the
Law of "Excluded Middle."

The third one of
"The Laws of Thought" (p. 205)
is not included in
this set of postulates,
but can be easily PROVED from them,
as a theorem,
in the following way:

To prove that $p = p$:

(1)		$p \cdot 1$	$= p$	Postulate	(4)
(2)	∴	$p (p \vee p')$	$= p$	Postulate	(9)
(3)	∴	$p \cdot p \vee p \cdot p'$	$= p$	Postulate	(7)
(4)	∴	$p \cdot p \vee o$	$= p$	Postulate	(10)
(5)	∴	$p \cdot p$	$= p$	Postulate	(3)
(6)	∴	$p \vee o$	$= p$	By substituting in Step (4)
(7)	∴	p	$= p$	Postulate	(3)

And so on;
you can interpret
the other postulates
and various theorems
derived from them.

---

† You remember that
$p \vee q$ means
either p or q or both (p. 206),
but in $p \vee p' = 1$
the case of BOTH p and p'
being true (i.e. $= 1$)
is ruled out by
Postulate (10) on p. 206.

Thus we see that
the Algebra of Propositions
is really analogous to
the two-valued
Algebra of Classes or
a two-valued
Boolean Algebra,
and we see clearly that
by means of it
we can handle only
a "universe of discourse" whose
propositions are either
strictly "true" or
strictly "false,"
as in Aristotelian Logic,.
in which
to the question
"Is this true?"
you must answer strictly
ONLY "YES" or "NO"!
Later you will see that
MODERN Logicians are now
going much further
and developing systems in which
you will no longer be limited to
Yes or No,—
undoubtedly you can even now
appreciate what a boon this can be!

You are now also in a position to
summarize briefly the
"hypothetical" and "disjunctive"
syllogisms,
since these belong to
the Algebra of Propositions,
as you will see in
the next chapter.

XXIII. STREAMLINING "MODUS PONENS,"
ET AL.

Since, in Logic,
we speak of
one proposition "implying" another,
it is important that
you know clearly
how the term "implication"
is related to the
Algebra of Propositions.
In order to express
this relationship,
we must use what is known as
"material implication"
(designated by the symbol $\supset$)
instead of the well-known
ordinary "implication" of
traditional Logic,—
the new term including
the old one.
For instance,
under the old meaning,
to say that "p implies q"
means that
from p you can INFER q,
that is,
if you know p to be true,
and if p implies q,
then you can infer that
q is also true.
Whereas

$$p \supset q$$

is DEFINED TO MEAN

$$p' \vee q$$

as used in the
Algebra of Propositions.
Now

$$p' \vee q$$

has, as you know,
a perfectly definite meaning
in the Algebra of Propositions,
whereas for the
ordinary "implication"
there is no operation here
corresponding to it;
but, fortunately,
these two kinds of
"implication"
are related,
so that we can,
by means of this Algebra,
see clearly what is involved in
the old meaning of
"implication" or "inference."
In order to do this,
let me introduce to you
what is known as
the "truth-table,"
a very useful and simple device:

Suppose we have
two propositions, p and q,
each of which may of course
have the value 1 or 0
(that is, it may be true or false).
Then the proposition

$$p' \vee q$$

formed from these
will of course also be
either true or false (1 or 0)

Let us therefore
tabulate all the possibilities
as follows
(remembering that
$p \supset q$ has been defined
to mean $p' \vee q$)—see p. 212.

p	q	p'	$p' \vee q$	$p \supset q$
1	1	0	1	1
1	0	0	0	0
0	1	1	1	1
0	0	1	1	1

Here the "truth-values" (1 or 0)
for p and q
are listed in all four
possible combinations:

p true and q true
p true and q false
p false and q true
p false and q false;

p', being the negation of p
(see page 205),
is false whenever p is true
and vice versa.
Now, by the definition of

$$p' \vee q$$

we know that it will be true
either if p' is true or
if q is true or
if both p' and q are true;
hence the values in
the column headed $p' \vee q$

are easily supplied
when the columns q and p'
have been previously filled in.
And, finally,
since $p \supset q$ has been
defined to mean $p' \lor q$ (p. 212),
these two columns
(those headed $p' \lor q$ and $p \supset q$)
will have the same values
all the way down.
And now note that
the old definition of
"implication,"
namely, that
"If p is true, and
  if it is true that
  p implies q, then
  q must be true"
is completely satisfied by
the first row of the table on p. 214.
And, furthermore,
the second row claims that
if p is true and q is false,
then it is false to say that
p implies q.
Hence,
the first two rows of the table
are consistent with the
old idea of implication,
and therefore
the new "material implication"
includes the old idea.
Do not worry too much about
the last two rows in the table,
which say that
when p is false,
it can "materially imply" that
q is either true or false!

For remember that
"material implication"
does NOT mean the same thing as
"implication" in the ordinary
sense of this word.
No doubt you are now
sufficiently sophisticated
to accept this new meaning,
just as you have already
accepted new meanings of
"addition," "multiplication," etc.
For this is
a modern device which has
proved to be
extremely useful,
as you know.

And we can now proceed to
express the
"hypothetical" and "disjunctive"
syllogisms,
by means of this Algebra,
as promised.

Thus,
take the pure hypothetical
syllogisms in

(1) Modus ponens (page 129).
    It is of the form:

    $p \supset q$ and $q \supset r$,
    therefore $p \supset r$,
    where p stands for
    the proposition A is B, etc.
    Let us make out
    the following "truth-table": *

* Remember that $p \supset q$ means $p' \vee q$, etc.

p	q	r	p'	q'	$p \supset q$	$q \supset r$	$p \supset r$
1	1	1	o	o	1	1	1
1	o	1	o	1	o	1	1
1	1	o	o	o	1	o	o
1	o	o	o	1	o	1	o
o	1	1	1	o	1	1	1
o	o	1	1	1	1	1	1
o	1	o	1	o	1	o	1
o	o	o	1	1	1	1	1

Note that wherever
$p \supset q$ and $q \supset r$ are both true (1)
then $p \supset r$ is also 1.
Hence this syllogism (p. 216)
is merely a statement of
the fact that
"material implication" is
TRANSITIVE:
this means that
any relationship, R, between
three elements (a, b, c)
such that
a R b and b R c gives a R c
is called "transitive."
For instance,
the relationship "equality"
is transitive because
if $a = b$ and $b = c$, then $a = c$.
But, if R represents
the relationship "is the father of,"
then
a R b and b R c
does NOT give a R c,
since in this case
a is NOT the father of c
but his grandfather.

Thus
some relationships are transitive
and some are not.
And, as you see from
the table on page 217,
MATERIAL IMPLICATION
IS TRANSITIVE,
since
whenever $p \supset q$ and $q \supset r$ are
both 1,
then
$p \supset r$ is also 1;
and thus
the pure hypothetical
"modus ponens"
is merely an illustration of
this statement.

Let us next look at

(2) Modus tollens (see top of p. 130).
It is of the form:

$p \supset q$ and $q \supset r'$,
therefore $r \supset p'$.

Here it will be necessary
to show first that

$$(p \supset q) \supset (q' \supset p').$$

Since $p \supset q$ means $p' \vee q$
and $q' \supset p'$ means $q \vee p'$,
we see that these
both mean the same thing
by Postulate (5) (page 206).
Thus
$q \supset r'$ may be replaced by $r \supset q'$
and $q' \supset p'$ may replace $p \supset q$.
Hence the premises of

this syllogism
may be written
$q' \supset p'$ and $r \supset q'$
or
$(q' \supset p') \cdot (r \supset q')$
or (by Postulate (6) on p. 206)
$(r \supset q') \cdot (q' \supset p')$.
Consequently,
by the transitive property (p. 217),
we get the conclusion:

$r \supset p'$

the required result.

Also for
the mixed hypothetical syllogisms:

(1) Modus ponens (p. 130) is:

$p \supset q$ is true ($= 1$)
and p is true ($= 1$),

therefore
from the table on p. 214
we get q is true.

(2) Modus tollens (near the bottom of p. 130):

$p \supset q$ is true and
q' is true.

Now since $p \supset q$ is equivalent to
$q' \supset p'$ (see p. 218)
we really have here

$q' \supset p'$ is true and
q' is true,
therefore p' is true
just as in
Modus ponens above.

Similarly for the other
hypothetical and disjunctive
syllogisms,
which you can work out
for yourself,
if you are interested.
Suffice it to say that
all of them can be done
by the use of
the same TWO principles:

(1) The transitive property of
material implication:

$p \supset q$ and $q \supset r$ gives $p \supset r$

and

(2) the fact that
the "negative converse" of
any proposition
has the same "truth-value" as
the proposition itself,
that is,

$p \supset q$ is the same as $q' \supset p'$

as shown on page 218.

And so,
if to the three lines on p. 162
(which summarize the original
categorical syllogisms)
you now add
these two principles, given above
(which summarize the
hypothetical and disjunctive
syllogisms),
you have,
in these five lines,

the entire subject of
traditional Logic,
as promised!
And you see that
they constitute only
a few of the theorems
which are possible in
Boolean Algebra!

And now let us
take a brief look at
the application to
electrical circuits,
that you may
further appreciate
the possibilities of
these
POWERFUL and SIMPLE
NEW METHODS!

XXIV. TURN ON THE LIGHT, SAM!

This is not the place
to describe
any applications of
Boolean Algebra to
"business";
anyone interested can
look them up.*
They are extremely interesting
and useful,
and,
as has happened so many times
in the course of
SAM's experience,
his games turn out to be
both ENTERTAINING and PRACTICAL.
Suffice it to say a little here
about C. E. Shannon,†
who made the application of
the two-valued Boolean Algebra
to electrical circuits.
He realized that
such a circuit is
"two-valued,"
since it can be only
either "closed" or "open";
and
back in his student days
he had studied

* See "Elementary Topics in Mathematical Logic"
   by A. Church (Galois Inst. Press, Long Island Univ.).
† Trans. of the
   Amer. Inst. of Elect. Eng.,
   vol. 57 (1938).

the two-valued Boolean Algebra.
Now, the connection between these two domains,
apparently so widely separated,
"clicked" in his mind,
and he became interested
in seeing whether
he could carry through successfully
this analogy.
And sure enough
he did it as follows:

He let the "elements" be
the switches, x, y, z, etc.,
and defined

$$x + y$$

to mean that
the switches x and y are
connected "in series," thus:

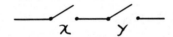

whereas

$$x \cdot y$$

is to mean that
they are connected "in parallel,"
like this:

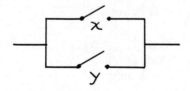

He then let o mean "closed"
and 1 mean "open."

You can see how
the following combinations
would affect the circuit.

SUMS

(switches "in series")

$$
\begin{array}{lll}
x & y & x+y \\
0 & +0 = & 0 \\
1 & +0 = & 1 \\
0 & +1 = & 1 \\
1 & +1 = & 1
\end{array}
\left.\rule{0pt}{7ex}\right\}
\begin{array}{l}
\text{according to} \\
\text{Boolean} \\
\text{Algebra.}
\end{array}
$$

That is,
if the switches are
connected "in series,"
the entire circuit $(x + y)$
is "closed" $(= 0)$ only if
BOTH switches are "on" $(= 0)$.

PRODUCTS

(switches "in parallel")

$$
\begin{array}{lll}
x & y & x \cdot y \\
0 & \cdot 0 = & 0 \\
1 & \cdot 0 = & 0 \\
0 & \cdot 1 = & 0 \\
1 & \cdot 1 = & 1
\end{array}
\left.\rule{0pt}{7ex}\right\}
\begin{array}{l}
\text{as per} \\
\text{Boolean} \\
\text{Algebra.}
\end{array}
$$

Here, where the switches are
"in parallel,"
the circuit is "closed" $(= 0)$
(i.e. the current can flow)
in ALL cases except only
when BOTH switches are
"open" $(= 1)$;
that is,.

$x = 1$ AND $y = 1$

is the only case in which

$$x \cdot y = 1.$$

Similarly,
he found that there was
a complete
"one-to-one correspondence"
between these circuits and
the two-valued Boolean Algebra,
so that by means of
the theorems in this Algebra
he was able to
solve problems like:

If there are four switches
(w, x, y, z) and
a motor
in a circuit,
what electrical connections
must be made so that
the motor will be "on" if

(1) any ONE of the switches is "on"
(2) any THREE of them are "on";

and so that
the motor will be "off" if

(3) any TWO of the switches are "on"
(4) all FOUR switches are "on."

You can easily believe that
this type of problem
would come up in a
telephone company's life!
But who would have thought that
it would be solved by
that funny little, abstract
Boolean Algebra?!

Naturally it took
one of SAM's men
to have the
IMAGINATION
to connect up his
SOPHISTICATED knowledge of
the ABSTRACT
with problems that
confront him in
his practical daily living.

Similarly,
another of SAM's men,
John von Neumann,‡
began an application
of other branches of
modern abstract mathematics
to the field of
Economics
(in collaboration with
an economist,
Oskar Morgenstern).

And of course
the great Einstein
derived the
atomic energy formula

$$E = mc^2$$

with the aid of
abstract mathematical
considerations,
and he now sees
the marvelous possibilities of
atomic energy

‡ See "Theory of Games and Economic Behavior"
by von Neumann and Morgenstern
(Princeton University Press).

for the BENEFIT of mankind—
do you wonder that
he is so anxious that
YOU
know about it,
so that you and your children
for generations
may have
a wonderful and abundant
LIFE!
Are YOU going to let the
ANTI–SAM–ITES
destroy you,
or are you going to follow
SAM
and be
HAPPY?!

XXV. GOOD–BYE FOR NOW

Thus you have learned
something about
the wonders of the
ABSTRACT
via Boolean Algebra.
You have seen it
simplify traditional Logic
and lead to
practical applications.

Undoubtedly
your own imagination
must have asked you:
But what about cases
in which
you cannot say just
"Yes" or "No,"
"True" or "False,"
"Closed" or "Open,"
as in the
Two-valued System?
And indeed
this IS a very
IMPORTANT question,
especially when you consider
how many problems
are erroneously FORCED
into this two-valued set-up.
Thus the opposing ideas of
"freedom of speech" or
"no freedom of speech,"—
"freedom of enterprise" or
"no freedom of enterprise,"

etc., etc.,
are NOT really just TWO-valued,
(all or none!),
but should be treated
as SAM handles the ideas of
"hot" or "cold":
thus,
if you perform the
following experiment,
much light will be shed for you
on this subject:

Take three vessels of water,
one (A) in which
the water is
as hot as you can stand it,
another (B) in which it is
as cold as you can stand it,
and the third (C) containing
lukewarm water at
room temperature.
Now put your right hand into A,
and your left into B,
and keep them there for a while.
If you then transfer
your right hand into C,
this water will seem
"cold" to you;
whereas if you transfer
your left hand into C,
this same water will seem
"warm" to you.
Thus our senses are
NOT
the best way to make
a "judgment."
And therefore
SAM prefers to use

a thermometer,
and not to bother with
the indefinite words
"hot" and "cold,"
but to express the temperature
in "degrees,"
thus allowing for
a great variety of
possible temperatures
instead of the two too naïve
"hot" and "cold."

And may it not be the same
with "freedom of enterprise"?
Might not either extreme
be undesirable for society?
And may there not perhaps
be an "optimum" point
somewhere along the line
which would be better than
either "all" or "none,"
as shown in the following diagram:

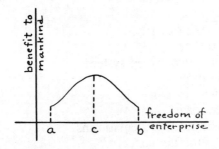

Might not too little
freedom of enterprise,
as at point a,
as well as too much,
as at b,
both be of less benefit

to mankind
than
at some intermediate point c?
No one really knows
where this optimum point is,
and it is therefore
a problem to be considered by
SAM
in the spirit
in which he always works,
and not by
arguments full of
all the old fallacies of
"ad hominem" (page 133),
ad this and
ad that
("odds buds")—
anything but
ad SAM, as they should be!

Thus SAM,
although he uses
the two-valued system
where it applies,
and there uses it expertly,
also realizes that
where such a two-valued system
does NOT apply,
he is the first to admit it
and to encourage
his Scientists and Mathematicians
to use the "function concept,"
which allows for
a large range of values,
(as in temperature measurements,
mentioned on page 231),
instead of only two.
Indeed,

even in Modern Logic itself,
new systems are
now being developed
which allow not only for
the two values
"true" or "false"
but also for
various degrees of
"probability"!
Of course
this is not the place
to go into
this new and important branch of
Logic.
Those interested
may wish to look up
"Symbolic Logic" by
Lewis and Langford.

And so,
till we meet again
let us all go back to
Part I of this book,
"The Emergency,"
and see to it that
there will be a world at all,
for,
as H. G. Wells so wisely observed,
there is a RACE on between
EDUCATION and CATASTROPHE!

But
if we go into it
with SAM at our side
to LEAD us,
we shall tackle it
in his spirit of

FAITH,
HOPE,
CHARITY,
JUSTICE,
MERCY,
HUMILITY,
INTELLIGENCE,
IMAGINATION,
MODERN REALISM,
MODERN ABSTRACT TOOLS—
in short,
with the essence of
what is best in
human nature.
This will restore
a well-justified faith in
human nature,
and will stop our
"knocking ourselves out"
with the slanderous views
about "human nature" which
make it a mere synonym for
hatred and greed.
Even granting that
there is in each one of us
a "bit of a stinker,"
still
why emphasize it out of all proportion?
Do you ever hear
anyone say on the radio,
right after the playing of
a Beethoven symphony,
"Isn't that a beautiful
  illustration of
  human nature?"
No! no one ever says that!
But when speaking of
thievery and murder and war,

THEN we hear
"There it is again—
 HUMAN NATURE!"
I ask you,
is that fair?!

Let us rather go along with
SAM
in his assertion that
greed, etc.,
are PATHOLOGICAL DISTORTIONS
of the legitimate desire to
"eat" (see Chapter VIII),
and that
the NORMAL functioning
of this urge
is in the direction of the
ABSTRACT
(after we have had
"enough" on the physical level)
for it is in the
ABSTRACT,
in creative
Science, Art, Mathematics,
that our urge to
"unite with" or
"love" or
"eat"
the whole world,
can go on and on
without our interfering with
each other.

XXVI. THE MORAL

As you have seen,
this little book
is an attempt to see what
MODERN REALISM
demands of us
in order to reward us with
SURVIVAL and HAPPINESS.

It therefore concerns itself with:

(1) An EMERGENCY program
(2) a long-term program of
    EDUCATION.

Obviously the EMERGENCY program
must consider the
ELIMINATION of WAR
(for otherwise
we just won't be here
to get educated!)
And since
modern warfare is
a matter of
WEAPONS of MASS DESTRUCTION,
we must consult SAM (p. 74)
in order to get the
FACTS,
without which
we cannot think
REALISTICALLY!
Here, then,

236

we MUST follow him,
the modern Paul Revere (p. 25),
who is trying to arouse us
to an awareness of
the DANGER—
and we must NOT follow
the lead of the
grossly uninformed,
who have the audacity
to say that
the modern weapons
have been
overrated!!

Then, if the human race
succeeds in
eliminating war,
it will
have to consider
what shall be our
ORIENTATION
in the future.
What kind of
philosophy of education
shall we need for
SURVIVAL and HAPPINESS?
What guide to
MORALITY,
and not to mere MORES?!

Those who are
truly religious
already have such a guide.
But those who do not follow
this guide,
as well as those
who merely use their creed

237

as a WEAPON to fight
other creeds,—
for all these
a guide,
an orientation,
a LEADER,
is desperately needed—
for NONE of us is safe
so long as there are
SOME who
either lead us to
destruction and death,
or who are
so CONFUSED
that they too drive us to
death and destruction.

Now,
NO PERSONAL LEADER
can fill the bill,
for no personal leader
knows enough or
lives long enough
to do the job.
And that is why
it has been here proposed
to follow
a character named SAM,
who is the ESSENCE of
what is best in
the human race itself.
And this little book
has tried to show, by
DOCUMENTARY EVIDENCE
from Science, Art, Mathematics
how we can actually
get help from
SAM

238

and how he can teach us to
recognize,
and protect ourselves from,
ANTI–SAM–ITES,
and how to
LIVE and be HAPPY!

While the name
SAM
is derived from
Science, Art, Mathematics,
its significance is wider than that: *
The S represents our contact with
FACTS,
with the
OUTSIDE WORLD;
the M represents
the REASONING power of our minds,
and
the A represents
our INTUITION,
which,
being between the S and M
is thus prevented from
going wild
(like Hitler's "intuition"),
but is checked by both
FACTS and REASON.
Thus,
if we follow
SAM,
we are led,
in the consideration of
any problem
to bring to bear upon it

* For further clarification of SAM
  see "INFINITY" by Lillian R. Lieber, with
  drawings by Hugh G. Lieber (1953).

S and A and M
in an INTEGRATED manner,
and stop being
the kind of
"split personality"
that, like the Nazis,
ignores facts and reason
and peddles lies,
or that,
like the defenders of
mere gadgets,
ignores the deep significance
of SAM's "A"
in "fundamental science."
It is interesting to test
SAM
in confused discussions,
for he really
can guide us through
the barrage of words
now attacking us
from every direction.

Let therefore
SAM,
who gets his inspiration
from the Lord Himself,
be
OUR LEADER.

"intuition."
Note that
in Chapter XVII,
all conclusions were drawn
"intuitively,"
and that was
acceptable as a tentative start,
but SAM demands
that results
must be derived by
meticulously showing
that they follow from the
BASIC POSTULATES,
and that nothing else
"sneaks in,"
either through carelessness
or by deliberate intent!

That is how
HONEST and CAREFUL
SAM is!

I. And so let us

PROVE $a \times o = o$ (or $a \cdot o = o$)

Proof

Statements	Reasons
(1) $(a \cdot o) = (a \cdot o) + o$	Postulate (3)
(2) $\quad\quad = o + (a \cdot o)$	Postulate (5)
(3) $\quad\quad = (a \cdot a') + (a \cdot o)$	Postulate (10)
(4) $\quad\quad = a(a' + o)$	Postulate (7)
(5) $\quad\quad = a \cdot a'$	Postulate (3)
(6) $\quad\quad = o$	Postulate (10)

And so it has been
PROVED
that $a \cdot o = o$

II. Here is another one:

To prove $ab' = 0 \longrightarrow a = ab$
That is:
If we have given that $ab' = 0$
we can PROVE from it that
$a = ab$:

Proof

Statements	Reasons
(1) $\qquad ab + 0 = ab$	Postulate (3)
(2) $\qquad\qquad ab' = 0$	Given
(3) $\therefore\ ab + ab' = ab$	Since $ab' = 0$
(4) $\therefore\ a(b + b') = ab$	Postulate (7)
(5) $\therefore\qquad a(1) = ab$	Postulate (9)
(6) $\therefore\qquad\quad a = ab$	Postulate (4)

If this result seems
"strange,"
please remember that
a and b are NOT numbers,
but CLASSES,
and what you have just proved
is shown in
the following diagram:

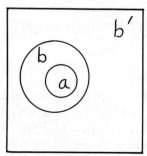

Here the rectangle is
the boundary within which
are all the classes of the set;
among them are a and b,
b' being the complement of b

(that is, the class containing
all the classes not in b);
hence $ab' = 0$ merely
expresses the fact that
a and b' have no classes in common
(and hence a is entirely within b).
And it has been proved
that the consequence of this is
that $a = ab$,
which simply means that
the part common to a and b
(represented, as usual, by ab)
is the class a itself,
a result which is
easily verified from
the diagram on p. 192.

Perhaps you are thinking that
you follow the argument better
from the diagram
than from the formal proof
written out on page 192.
But of course you must realize that:

(1) "intuitional" ideas
    require "checking";
    the "feeling" that
    we are right
    may be misleading!

(2) whenever we are trying
    to learn to use
    any new machine,
    we are a little unhappy about it
    at first.
    Thus when learning
    to drive a car
    you can no doubt
    walk around the block

more easily than
you can drive around,
but nevertheless,
if you learn to drive,
you will then have
a means of
"going places"
that you could never have if
you stuck to walking.
And so, here,
you are learning to use
Boolean Algebra,
basing all your arguments
on its postulates
and not on
any other consideration,
such as diagrams, etc.,
though whenever such
diagrams help you,
you may use them to guide you,
though they are NOT acceptable
in a formal proof—
since strict reliance on
the postulates
has been found to be
the safest method.
And, indeed,
in more difficult problems,
you will find that
these diagrams
are no longer so helpful,
so the wise thing is
to practice
and get skill
in formal proofs.

And now let us PROVE
Barbara and Darii.